*Bab*

G000277440

# *Baby* Green

## CARING FOR YOUR BABY
## THE ECO-FRIENDLY WAY

*Jill Barker*
*with Gilly Smith*

**GAIA**
THINKING

An Hachette Livre UK Company

First published in Great Britain in 2007 by
Gaia, a division of Octopus Publishing Group Ltd
2–4 Heron Quays, London E14 4JP
www.octopusbooks.co.uk

ISBN-13: 978-1-85675-134-6
ISBN-10: 1-85675-134-1

A CIP catalogue record for this book is available from the British Library

Printed and bound in Italy

Printed on Cyclus Offset, a 100 per cent recycled paper

10 9 8 7 6 5 4 3 2 1

This book is not intended as a substitute for medical advice. The reader
should consult a physician on all matters relating to health. While the advice
and information are believed to be accurate and true at the time of going to
press, neither the author nor the publisher can accept legal responsibility or
liability for any errors or omissions that may have been made.

# CONTENTS

Introduction                                          7

Chapter 1  The health of the planet                  23
Chapter 2  The health of your baby                   45
Chapter 3  Food and health                           75
Chapter 4  Greening the nursery                      99
Chapter 5  What a waste                             127
Chapter 6  Greening the bathroom                    151
Chapter 7  Greening your wardrobe                   175
Chapter 8  Travelling green                         199
Chapter 9  How green is your childcare?             217

Resources                                          231
Index                                              259
Acknowledgements                                   272

# INTRODUCTION

# the story of Green Baby

I can't say that I was always green. I was just one of the
millions of foreigners who went to London to earn a bit of
cash to go travelling, and who found a guy, had a baby, and
what do you know? Suddenly I became an eco-pioneer!
Maybe I learnt a few skills along the way, but looking back, I'm
not sure that it was any more complicated than that. Perhaps
just following your instinct, asking questions and finding your
own solutions really can help change the world.

Sometimes the whole issue of the environment, climate
change and statistics about waste can seem terribly
complicated. You need a science degree to understand some
of the stuff they throw at you on the news, and you're often
left feeling helpless and guilty. Being a new parent, you
can feel overwhelmed by the weight of responsibility
not just for your life but of your growing family;
your new baby seems so incredibly dependent
on you. Forget the hormonal fallout; I'm sure
that it's that mind-blowing reality hit that brings
on those baby blues, and the prospect of
tripling your waste output is enough to make
you put your hands over your ears and pretend
it's not happening.

Well, as someone whose life changed completely
with the birth of my child, I'm here to tell you that it's a
lot easier than you might think. A lot of you will be up to
speed on the basics already. Who doesn't know that if you
refuse to recycle, you're contributing to the apocalypse that
we've been promised? Most of us have seen *The Day After*

*Tomorrow*, haven't we? But have we all seen Al Gore's *The Inconvenient Truth*? This book should fast-track you through the politics and the prose, taking you on a whistle-stop tour through the supply chains behind all your baby products and putting the whole story together. From the cotton fields of India to the acacia forests of Poland, you'll get a rare insight into what Fairtrade clothing and sustainable wooden shelves really mean. If you emerge buying washable nappies and using eco balls, I'll have done my job.

# *how it all began*

My story is of a mother who followed her instinct and became a successful businesswoman. I make no bones about telling you that when I spotted a gap in the natural baby products market, I went straight for it. It meant that my little boy wore elephant-design 100 per cent organic cotton washable nappies, I bathed his early eczema in a soothing chamomile milk bath, and he stretched out on Fairtrade bedding in a cot that changed into three different sizes of bed as he grew up, but so did a brand-new market of parents who also wanted the best for their children and for the planet. I asked the questions, found the answers and an enormous number of people are still buying them. As the news about environmental damage gradually sinks into our cultural psyche, necessity is the mother of invention.

What I found out along the way made me ask even more questions rather than sit back complacently with the answers that I had found. Ethical retail is a Pandora's box of issues, and many of them are still not resolved. My job is to source the best products, to try and make sure that the supply chain is fairly treated, that the money I make from my business flows back into the world that made it, and that the consumer understands that behind every nappy, every babygro, every toy, there's a whole team of people who have picked, cut, stitched, dyed and packed it under the best possible conditions. Your job as the consumer is to understand that not everyone gets the same deal, and to insist that they do.

I'm no climatologist; I even bunked off science at school and I can barely pronounce some of the chemicals Greenpeace found in disposable nappies but I ask a lot of questions and I find a lot of great people who know what they're talking about. I also trust my instinct and good old-fashioned common sense. I know that if a baby's bottom sits in a nappy full of perfumes and lotions, his skin will absorb it. If a child wears pyjamas sprayed with flame retardant, he's going to breathe it in while he's asleep. If plastic bottles leach strange-sounding chemicals beginning with 'Phth' into my baby's milk, I'm going to use glass.

My husband, Jonathan, and I met at the bank where we both worked. We were the quintessential high-life city flyers, Mr and Mrs Yuppy, suited and booted, double-incomed and certainly no kids. Before I got pregnant we were barely ever at home. In fact if you ask how green I was, I couldn't really tell you because I had no way of measuring our waste. Did I recycle? I didn't have anything to recycle because I was never home. Of course whenever I went back to see my family in Canada, everyone I knew was into recycling, but my London was a place where you didn't really think in those terms. We consumed like there was no tomorrow, but it tended to be good food and a lot of alcohol rather than anything that could be put into the correct bins.

It would be so easy to say that it was the consumer society of London life that had seduced me, that I was living in a dream-world of spending – or maybe it was a nightmare of capitalist hell – until motherhood jolted me into a new reality. But, you know what? I don't think I was thinking of anyone other than myself. And that suited me just fine.

When I got pregnant, Jonathan and I were in shock. We hadn't planned this at all. You'd think that Green Jill would have been detoxing – both the liver and the flat, repainting the nursery with eco-paints, stocking up on organic, locally produced fruit and vegetables (in Islington?) and signing up for inspiring baby magazines, but no. Yuppy Jill was too busy having a good time out on the town while she still could. No yoga or active birth classes for me. No water birth at home for this old Pisces; I was signing up for the epidural before I unpacked my overnight bag.

When Thomas came along, our not so little Halloween pumpkin, weighing in at a colossal 4.3 kg (9 lb 10 oz) on

31 October 1998, there was suddenly someone else to worry about. But I didn't think, 'Right, now I really should start thinking about the planet.' On the contrary; I was thrown into a world where I was thinking 'Oh my God, what do I do now?' I remember talking to my friends and asking which nappies they used, whether they were Huggies or Pampers; there only seemed to be two brands. I suppose I vaguely thought that they were rather expensive, and I even tried buying own-label nappies for a while to save some money.

It was two months into this new experience of motherhood when Thomas got the rash that changed the direction of my life. He was just a tiny little thing, lying on his back kicking his legs in the air when I noticed a weird-looking gel on his bottom. I thought it was coming out of him at first and ran to the phone to ask one of my very few maternal friends if I should I rush him to the hospital. She laughed at my hysteria and told me not to worry. It was just what was inside the nappies, she said, and sometimes it leaked. She said that she was sure it was harmless, unless you accidentally put one in the washing machine like she had done the previous week – a very costly accident that meant she had had to replace her washing machine. (I have since learned that she didn't really need to replace her machine – running a load with salt in it would have solved her problem because the salt breaks down the nappy gel.)

I remember considering the rather revolting idea of chemicals being in a nappy, but must have dismissed it pretty quickly. I asked her about the rash and she said not to worry, that it was just nappy rash. I wasn't convinced by my friend's argument and took him to the doctor who confirmed that the red sores and welts were typical of nappy rash and advised me to use a zinc-based nappy cream to calm it down. He told me that the usual cause of nappy rash is the skin being kept in wet or soiled nappies for too long. Stale urine, he informed me, creates ammonia, which can break down the protective barrier on the skin. Germs then form and can cause redness and inflammation. Hardly a big deal, he assured me; it happens to most babies. I think he might have suggested that I leave the nappy off as much as possible, but he didn't seem to be at all concerned when I asked him about the gel. What harm could it possibly do?

But Thomas hadn't been sitting in wet nappies. I'd been checking his nappy every couple of hours and scratching my head because it just wasn't wet. Surely he must have peed in the last two hours? If not, why hadn't he? When my mother was looking after Thomas one day, she had left his nappy on for hours because it just wasn't wet. When I found out that the gel had been absorbing it all, I was horrified. He hadn't just been sitting in his own urine, but in a fruity little cocktail of pee and unidentified chemicals!

# my quest for real nappies

I began to do some research. It just didn't seem right to put my little baby in a pad packed with God knows what. I soon discovered that some babies' skin is more sensitive than others, and that they can react to some of the components of disposable nappies. The lotions, perfumes and the chemical super-absorber 'gel', it seemed, may be the cause of nappy rash in some chemically sensitive babies. When I read that the skin is an organ and that it doesn't just react to these chemicals but it absorbs them too, my inner lioness leapt out to protect my little cub and I went straight onto the Internet to find an alternative.

When Thomas was about three months old, I took him back home to Canada to meet my family, and I mentioned the issue of nappies to one of my cousins. Canadians have been tapped into environmental issues for years and seemed much more sophisticated about it than we were in the UK. She told me that everyone she knows uses washable nappies. 'Don't you know about them?' she asked me in disbelief. 'They're the latest thing.'

She took me shopping and we spent the day looking at the endless number of washable nappies on offer. They were in department stores and pharmacies; there were even specialist nappy shops on the high street!

Washable nappies seemed to have come such a long way over the years. I was so impressed by the amount of information the shops had and how committed they all were to changing the way we think about these things. Their energy was infectious. And this was the high street! I stocked up on a whole set of them and brought them back to England with me.

Thomas was four months old when I went back to work in January 1999. I had put him down for a place at a nursery in the City, and like so many little banking babies, he was there from 8 a.m. to 6 p.m. But things in the City were not so good for women at the end of the last century, and once I'd discovered that all my major accounts had been given away while I was on maternity leave, I wasn't too surprised when I was offered a redundancy package only a few weeks after I'd started back at work.

Luckily, it was enough of a redundancy package to use to take some time off to get used to my new life as a mother. Jonathan still had his job, so there wasn't too much of a financial imperative for me to find a new job immediately.

It was when I ran out of my Canadian supply of washables (Thomas was growing so fast) that I began to do some research into where I could get more. I looked around to see if anyone was selling them by mail order and although there were a few companies doing it, I realized that they hadn't really arrived in the UK. A glimmer of a business idea popped into my head and I decided to do some more digging.

I quickly came across the Real Nappy Association (RNA) (which is currently accessible through WEN) and the Women's Environmental Network (WEN), which were both campaigning for real nappies and were based in London. They sent me a list of all the places that sold washables and we got chatting. I told them about my experience in Canada and they told me about what they were trying to do. I decided to volunteer for them.

Part of my work would involve going out to market stalls with a big board with all these different types of nappies pinned on to it, and talking to people about them and about why they should use washables. I went to Spitalfields Market in London every Sunday for a couple of months, and Thomas and Jonathan would come down with me. As far as I know WEN are still there every Sunday with that old nappy board. People who haven't discovered nappies think that there are only terries on the market, and when they see the different options, they think, 'Wow, we really need to know about this.' It really wasn't very difficult to get them interested. It was far more difficult for that poor composting campaigner on the stall next to me!

# *the birth of Green Baby*

People seemed to be really keen and wanted to know where they could buy them, and that glimmer of an idea began to occupy more of my brain. The couple of mail order suppliers of the nappies I was using for Thomas were importing them from Canada, so I started bulk buying from them. Now when people asked for washables while I was out on the street, I could say, 'Well, actually I have some right here. And here's my number for when you run out.'

It seemed obvious to me that there was a real gap in the market, although how to fill it seemed to be so complicated to everyone else I talked to about it. It didn't really need to be; wasn't it just a case of importing washables and selling them? That's kind of what I'm about, I suppose; I ask the questions and make things simple. It's like the grocery delivery scheme; everyone wants to do it, so let's just make it easy.

Even though I was still only a volunteer for WEN, my market was already beginning to expand. One of the midwives at a hospital in London had invited me to talk to all the new mums about washables as part of the antenatal classes she offered, and when I asked her if I could sell to them too, she was delighted. So I went to talk to these expectant parents and I took a selection of nappies along. I told them about my experiences as a mum and how easy it was to use them. They were so pleased and thankful! I got a couple of sales there, and they continued buying from me after they had their babies.

With the little trickle of orders coming in from my Spitalfields customers and my antenatal classes at the hospital, word was getting around. My first big mail order was from a couple of actors. I remember them ringing up and saying that they were going off filming and they needed to buy up a whole load of nappies. They ordered around £200 ($395) worth of washable nappies! It makes me smile now when I think how excited I was.

But I was beginning to think about something really quite radical; I would set up the first nappy shop on the British high street. I remember the conversations I had with friends over dinner when I told them that I was going to open a shop on Islington high street and fill it with real nappies. They would look at me in horror and say 'What? What do you know about retail?' I'd have to say that I knew absolutely nothing. I assured them that I wasn't worried because the people who were moving out were leaving the cash register.

On a hunch, I decided to get my trademark registered. I have no idea how come I knew to do that. I had this name, this fantastic name. When I looked up 'Green Baby' and saw that it was available, I couldn't believe it. How come no one had trademarked it? I just had to have that name. It cost thousands of pounds for each category so I just registered for everything; baby foods, carriers, toys, anything to do with babies that was on the list, I ticked. I suppose it forced me to have a vision. I had only been thinking about nappies but as I was wading though all these categories, I was thinking 'that's interesting. I could do that'. I would then have to find all these natural baby products, and maybe the really green ones that I wanted didn't even exist yet, but that process was the making of the shop. I was beginning to get really excited.

The shop made money pretty much straight away. I remember doing the figures and my father-in-law laughing at me when I told him how many nappies I had to sell in a week to pay the rent. Well I did that on the first day. I needed to sell £500 ($987) worth of nappies that day to cover my costs and I just made it. The green network had really helped to put me on the map; if people asked WEN or RNA where they could buy washables, they would say, 'Well there's this great little shop that's opened in Islington.' Word of mouth was a big help; the great thing about the shop was that people would talk to each other about the real practicalities of being a green parent. There would be customers in there all the time who would tell it how it is, why nappies leak, how to put them on properly, what to do when you're out and about. People love to talk about poo!

I had a shop full of nappies that was doing really well and a mail order service that was also ticking over nicely. I'd spent a lot of time talking to people in the green world about products and their impact on the environment, and I also knew that my customers were really into this stuff. I added to my range of nappies to include products from all over the world that were making green parents even greener, and un-green parents really switched on to the whole debate. This was fun, and maybe it could even change the world!

The environment was becoming the hot topic and more companies were moving into it. Becoming a parent in the new millennium was creating a new 'self-interested' market, according to the think tank, the Future Foundation, and was making Britain greener. And this time, it wasn't just hype; the market was backing my instincts.

# Green Baby today

In 2007, we have four shops in the UK. Our products sell across the world now, from garden centres to department stores. A Green Baby shop has just opened in Taipei and we are now looking at opportunities in other countries.

I love to think of myself as a pioneer. It makes me sound like one of a small band of hardy folk who took a deep breath and followed their hearts despite all the obvious pitfalls along the way. Actually my path was pretty easy – we were really fortunate that we did what we did at the right time in the right place. It means that I can now spend more time looking around the world and seeing what kind of products could do with my support. Everything at Green Baby comes from asking questions, and now that we have learnt so much from them, I would love to spend the rest of my life finding new products that support more social projects around the world.

But being green is also a mindset; it's about asking 'why?' Once you start thinking things through, you can't stop. You get to thinking about all sorts of weird things like why is it that Western children take so long to be potty trained? Is it because they don't share bathroom time with their parents? Are their parents even around enough to show them what to do?

And what about all those little safety catches that are supposed to stop toddlers destroying your house? Some of my friends have them in their houses and when their children come over to see us, they have no idea how to behave. They think, 'Hey, I can get into these cupboards.' How are children supposed to learn what they can and what they can't touch if you don't let them experiment with the real world? I know people who put bubble wrap around the edges of their coffee tables! It's like cutting off a cat's whiskers. What's next?

All this represents an over-protective response that doesn't help the child at all. But I suppose that the same impulse was what turned me from Mrs Yuppy into Green Jill. When you are childless you only have to think about yourself and maybe a significant other, now you have to think about getting that foetus into the world and that kid through his day, and you have to be much more responsible.

Julia Roberts said she was transformed into an environmentalist with the birth of her twins. In *Vanity Fair* magazine in 2006, she wrote 'People think, well I won't be here when the planet implodes, but maybe your grandchildren will or your great-grandchildren or your great-great-grandchildren will. And if you could give them one more day on earth, wouldn't you do that for them?'

# chapter one

# THE HEALTH OF THE PLANET

# *a changing agenda*

When I set up Green Baby, my main concern was to use what I had learned about green baby-friendly products to meet the needs of an emerging market. Today I'm much more aware of the wider environmental issues involved in every aspect of how we live our lives.

The arguments about global warming are now mainstream. Back then, there was even doubt about whether or not there was such a thing! If there was, it probably wasn't anything to do with us. You think poor old Al Gore would have lost his chance to become President of the United States of America in 2000 if people had believed him when he warned us that time was running out? Imagine what might have been achieved by now if he had been given that chance. As a result of George Bush winning the election, most people around the world in 2007 know just what it means that America still hasn't signed up to the Kyoto agreement.

For parents in particular, the fact that climate change has hit the top of the news agenda has been an opportunity to wise up – which was great timing for me and my business! People still come into the shop and say, 'What do I need to do to save the planet?' It's hard to be complacent when you've got a new child, or one on the way; there are so many things to look forward to, so many dreams and aspirations. When you finally grasp that the way you live your life will have a direct impact on your kid, you are definitely going to get your act together.

As a new parent, or parent to be, you will want to change the world. You'll protect the planet because it's where your new baby lives and nothing will stand in the way of ensuring he is safe. It would be weird not to. But knee-jerk responses won't help. You've got around nine months to think about the life that you're going to lead, so sit down and have a cup of tea (filling the kettle with just enough water for one) and consider what this debate is really all about.

## what's it all about?

Green campaigners tend to summarize the issues facing us as coming down to a few key principles:

- Climate change is real and very serious. Our lifestyle has an impact on carbon emissions and as oil becomes scarcer, our lifestyles will have to change

- Waste is a huge environmental problem – both its disposal and the energy used in the manufacture of items we throw away – and it fundamentally affects our eco-system

- The gap between the wealthy First and poverty-stricken Third Worlds is growing ever wider, and we need a system of fair trade to be statutory

# climate change: it's serious

So this is a big one, and may be beyond you, me and our friends to solve, but there are relevant choices we can make that can have an impact on carbon emissions, which most scientists now agree are influencing the climate. The mantra to learn is 'reduce, reuse, recycle', but already the papers are poking fun at eco-snobs and accusing businesses of making money out of global warming in a bid to distract us from what we know we have to do. So let's remind ourselves of the basics before we work out a plan of action.

## oil

For years, environmental lobbyists have been telling us that oil is a finite resource, that one day if we don't stop wasting it, it will run out. And we didn't listen. Now we're in what experts are calling the Peak Oil Age when we have to rethink our entire philosophy of life. As Jonathan Porritt told the annual Soil Association Conference in Cardiff in January 2007, we have to change our mindset from 'infinity and beyond' to 'finitude and beyond'. We have to accept that there is a limit – for the sake of our children.

After the glory days of expansionism warped our brains into believing that we could control the planet and do with it what we wanted, 50 countries have already passed their peak production and we are now in the long decline towards the end of energy as we know it. It's up to us all to make the changes, especially if you have a new baby, or one on the way; an eco-minority just won't do it this time.

Parent power really can lead the way in changing the future; we're the ones painting the nursery, fixing up new furniture, buying a wardrobe full of new clothes and filling the larder with healthier foods, so make your decisions green decisions; paints, lubricants, plastics, synthetic clothes, medicines, all the chemical-filled products that I'm urging you to ditch for the sake of your child and the planet, are all made from oil. As oil production is about to peak and move into decline, let's look at the alternatives now and impress our friends with our state of the art ideas!

We're going to have to do so soon enough; oil is at the very heart of our lifestyles. Right now, petrol doesn't only get us to the supermarket, but it also gets our food onto the shelves in the first place. Unless we eat organic food, the pesticides soaked into our produce are also made from the stuff. What about the energy used to light up our homes, turn on our TV, wash our clothes or simply to play music? Just about everything we do in our homes is fossil-fuel and petrochemical powered. It all comes from oil. What are we going to do? Wait until it runs out and then panic? That's just not what parents do. We plan for the future.

## carbon emissions

Scientists are not just concerned about the depletion of oil; the excessive use of it is raising temperatures in more than the skies. Politicians, the public and even retailers finally accept that carbon emissions are accumulating in the atmosphere much faster than scientists expected, with sea ice failing to fully refreeze for two winters running now. The impact is already devastating; Greenpeace and the World Health

Organization have both said that climate change already kills 160,000 people every year through drought and flooding, the spread of malaria and dengue fever. Within 50 years, they predict that one-third of our species could face extinction, not to mention the endless other species, big and small, which will be killed off by the changes in the eco-system. By the end of the century, says *Nature* magazine, Bangladesh will be no more, and major cities including New York and London will be lost to the sea.

Even in the prevaricating UK, it will soon be law to reduce our carbon emissions under a long-term plan to cut them in half by 2050. So how will we do it? Cut down our foreign travel? Get our kids to play outside all day rather than watch TV? Drive hybrid cars that run on electricity in towns and petrol on the fast roads? Rediscover the newly subsidized train? Yes, all of these and more. Twenty-five per cent of our emissions currently come from the energy we use in our everyday life; turning off the lights and using low energy bulbs, switching plugs off at the socket rather than leaving TVs and computers on standby all night, using the washing machine when you need to rather than for a small wash – it all makes a difference to the overall emissions depleting our precious oil reserves and heating up the planet.

Heating our homes heats the planet, yet simple measures such as turning down the room thermostat by just one degree, insulating the wall cavities and loft and replacing or repairing draughty windows and doors with double glazing can save around 75 per cent of your home's energy needs. Taking responsibility for how much energy you use in the home is essential, yet most of us haven't a clue. Upgrading or setting your controls properly for heating and hot water will help enormously in taking control of something we've always taken for granted.

Alternative forms of heating are appearing on the market which use renewable wood, wood chips or wood pellets and will save you money as well as reduce your dependence on fossil fuels. Woodburners are not just lovely to have as the centrepiece in your sitting room, but heat the whole house as opposed to those old-fashioned open fires that often meant draughty chimneys letting all the heat escape.

The power of the sun will also reduce your energy bills and carbon footprint, with councils giving grants for solar panels and DIY shops selling them for a fraction of the price they were ten years ago. If you're at home with your new baby, consider enlarging your windows. Babies love a warm comfortable environment, and solar gain means you could have a hot house even in the middle of winter without even turning the heating on. Eco-architects will advise you to have a dense floor such as marble to trap the heat and cool the house down in summer as well as keep it warm in winter. You're also less likely to suffer from seasonal affective disorder (SAD) due to lack of sunlight in a glass-sided house, something that will help the emotional ups and downs of new parenthood.

> *Calculating your carbon footprint and reducing it is the first step towards greening up your life.*

# *what we can do as parents*

I believe we're about to see a massive explosion of new energy-saving, reusable products on the market as people realize that climate change is a massive retail opportunity. There are plenty of products out there already that make life easier, cheaper and lighter on energy consumption, such as solar powered and wind up radios, Hippo water savers which save 2.5–3.5 litres (4–6 pints) of water when fitted in an average cistern of 9 litres (16 pints) capacity, or eco balls or aqua discs that can be used instead of washing liquid or powder.

They are great ideas, but many remind you that it's common sense that will save the planet; eco balls are supposed to produce ionized oxygen that activates the water molecules naturally, which then penetrate deeply into clothing fibres to dissolve the dirt. To all intents and purposes, they operate on much the same principle used by washerwomen all over the world; they simply bash that dirt out. Most stains are soluble in warm water anyway, but if eco balls don't quite get your whites right, you can always save them up for one really hot wash every couple of days. In the meantime, think about your purse; eco balls are reusable for up to 1,000 washes and cost on average 3p (5 cents) per wash and the rinse cycle can be shortened, which saves water and electricity. They are all examples of simple old ideas that look good and save the planet. And there will be plenty more.

And it's not just new products that I think will make their mark on the greener market; the Mooncup, a reusable menstrual cup made from soft silicone rubber has been around for years, but because it can save you a fortune over the years, as well as avoiding energy consumption and unnecessary chemicals being leached into the water supply, it could even replace tampons in our brave new world.

Washable nappies were a thing of the past rather than the future, but today they have a very important part to play in how we become greener parents. They won't just save you money over your baby's nappy-wearing years, but will also leave space for the less enlightened at the landfill. It's the same with organic cotton clothing, which will not only last long enough to be passed on to two or three more babies, but will also create employment opportunities in the developing world.

Glass bottles also used to belong to a bygone generation but are back to save the earth. They are not only reusable but won't leach chemicals into your baby's milk and then into the soil, polluting, mutating and killing many species in the wider eco-system unlike some of their plastic alternatives. And while you're feeding your baby from glass, how about calling your milkman back and having one van deliver the neighbourhood milk in recyclable glass bottles?

The more we leave our own car at home and share lifts and deliveries, the more we're likely to discuss our own domestic solutions to climate change and learn from each other about what's new on the market, or plan something green to do with the kids such as starting a wormery. If information overload has been one of the main reasons why most of us have done so little so far to reduce our carbon footprint, then chatting over green floor cleaners with a neighbour or watching the kids play with worms is more likely to kick us out of our stupor than any media campaign.

## waste

Most of us contribute more waste when we have a child than at any other time in our lives. While most parents are able to understand the arguments about how much waste disposable nappies create, the really big issue for them is time. New parents are suddenly so busy, doing all that essential stuff like putting his coat on, finding he needs changing again, putting his coat back on again, giving him a feed because you might not be able to when you get to the café, putting his coat on again... People cancel social outings for less. I don't mean to make fun of parents who get trapped into this mindset; I know how stressful it is trying to organize the simplest things in life with a new baby, but the answer really is in taking more time to do less, spend less and enjoy him more.

## reuse

Parents spend an average of £10,000 ($19,824) in the first year of their baby's life, but on what? We carry more unnecessary paraphernalia from sterilizers to baby wipes than we have ever done before and ever will again. It's mad to think what we packed to go away for a weekend when Thomas was little. Now that he's eight, I wonder what happened to it all. All

> # ❛Use it up, wear it out, make it do or do without.❜
> New England proverb

those toys I thought he couldn't do without, the things to stimulate him and to calm him down, to read to him, to play to him on long train journeys – where are they now? How come I didn't think to ask for his cousin's hand-me-downs? Did I honestly think that he wouldn't be interested in her Thumbelina CD?

## reduce

We have to get into the habit of thinking whether we even need those plastic toys and perfumed wipes in the first place. If we can do without it, we're not only reducing *our* carbon footprint but also the manufacturer's who, if enough of us follow the same principle, will soon have to reduce his output or change his ways. And that means less energy consumption, fewer carbon emissions and a bit more oil to go around – for a while at least.

## recycle

As a parent, you'll be chucking out and sorting through more than you ever did as a single person. Clothes will last weeks rather than years, high chairs will be rejected, nappies will pile high until your bin bags will be stuffed to the brim. Recycling still means sorting out what you can keep and what you need to get rid of, but you're reducing your carbon footprint dramatically by passing the clothes on to a charity shop, using websites like Freecycle (see Resources) to offload your high chair, and switching to washable nappies, which can then be either used again or passed on to the next baby.

The main point of recyling is to reduce the amount of rubbish going to landfill sites and the gases they would otherwise emit there. It also means a reduction of the need to resource new materials in the first place. But recycling is still in its infancy and, as such, not of great value. Bungles have been made such as the exporting of our waste halfway across the world to China without a thought of the impact of those miles on the environment, but lessons have been learnt from them. The UK government even set up a department, WRAP (the Waste and Resources Action Programme) in 2000 to concentrate on this as yet largely untapped potential and develop new markets.

The issue is around how much recycling we have to sell. While plastic bottles are sold for £200 ($396) per tonne, we need to recycle a hell of a lot more plastic bottles, and some councils still don't even accept plastic because it's just not worth their while. Aluminium cans at £700 ($1,387) per tonne are a much better cash cow, but it takes 60,000 cans to make a tonne – and that's a lot of dog food!

## retail therapy

Recycling means manufacturing fewer goods from scratch, which as manufacturing is one of the biggest consumers of oil, means less depletion of the little that is left; it takes roughly 20 barrels of oil or 3,818 litres (840 gallons) to produce just one average car for example.

It's not just cars of course; just think how much the mass-market retail industry uses in energy consumption, and with it comes plastic packaging that cannot be properly recycled yet. Add to that the conditions under which most manufacturing in the world is carried out, and we need to radically rethink how to shop. Again, while most reasonable adults can understand the arguments, few are prepared to change their shopping habits now that it has become a key part of their leisure time.

Aspiration is one of the biggest contributors to global waste, as we constantly dump and restock to keep up with the next trend, but if the retail giants are to be believed, they are on course to shift our mindset to aspire to buy Fairtrade or from the increasing number of cool new eco-designers. The cars and clothes of the future may well become must-have items if the new breed of green brains being recruited into manufacturing has anything to do with it.

# retail giants lead the way

We've all heard about Marks & Spencer's plans for becoming carbon neutral by 2012, working right through the supply chain to ensure fairness in trade and the lowest emissions possible, and how Whole Foods, the American organic supermarket, is taking London by storm with its honesty-bins and minimal but recyclable packaging, but now the rest of our supermarkets are frantically trying to do so too.

In 2006, the National Consumer Council found that UK retail giants need to work harder to cut their environmental damage. It looked at the way they source seasonal food and organics and deal with waste, and found that food production, storage, and transportation account for one-fifth of greenhouse gas emissions in the UK. Each person per household throws away £428 ($848) a year in food waste, amounting to a third of its weekly shop. But supermarkets are now signing up to deal with this, with giants like Tesco making radical promises about reducing their carbon footprint all the way through the supply chain.

But while they will tempt us with greener products and better sourcing policies, being green comes back to the issue of waste every time; clothes, food, cars, even furniture is all thoughtlessly dumped and unnecessarily replaced in our consumer culture, and while the manufacturers count the cash, their carbon emissions continue to cook the planet. When was the last time you saw anyone getting out a needle and thread to mend a pair of socks? The clothing industry has made it all so cheap by exploiting workers in the developing world, that there's little need to spend precious time on darning when you can get a new pair for next to nothing.

The principle of waste has deeply penetrated our consciousness; we're always looking for something new. As a new parent, you may have skipped straight to the chapter on preparing the nursery already, dreaming of cute little cots and pretty baby bedding. The idea of buying second-hand, reusing a cot and saving on the energy used in manufacturing may not be what you imagined, but it is the best way to reduce your baby's carbon footprint before he's even born!

All right, so you want your pretty little cot and frilly bedding, and you can have it! But consider how long it might last before you decide to buy. A bed that grows with your child, a mattress that won't be clogged with bugs by the time he's a toddler and organic cotton bedding that will last long enough to keep him warm when he's five years old will not only save you a lot of money over the next years, but that child of yours is going to be a zero-carbon kid by school age!

The next step is to tell him. The story of how a T-shirt came to be on his back will tell a small boy all he needs to know about how to shop when he's big enough. Kids pick this stuff up easily; my eight-year-old is a real little campaigner already and it's not because of my preaching (I hope). Quite simply, he gets it. He gets the fact that pesticides hurt the people who pick the chemical-doused cotton in the fields of India and Africa. He gets that Fairtrade means being fair about who you trade with. He gets the message because it's right, and kids are the most moral beings on the planet. Being a green parent is about making the future right for the consumers of tomorrow and being a great role model right now.

# how to reduce your carbon footprint

Textiles and the stories throughout the supply chain are the drivers behind my business; getting involved with organic cotton really did change the way I see the world. It's about understanding more than the fact that your baby's skin will absorb and accumulate the chemicals in synthetic materials; it's about realizing that over 14 million tonnes of synthetic fibre are produced each year from oil, an unrenewable resource that pollutes as it is extracted and is not biodegradable.

It's also about recognizing that there's a story behind that cotton babygro, with real people working the fields and the machines to get it to your baby. It's about the exploitation of children in manufacturing, the estimated three million pesticide-related deaths a year, and environmental contamination caused by persistent, mobile, bio-accumulative toxins used to control pests in poor countries. It is about the fact that conventional cotton makes up 3 per cent of the world's crops, yet uses 25 per cent of all insecticides and 10 per cent of all pesticides.

It was so exciting to be filling a genuine gap in the market with the first mainstream range of organic cotton baby clothes on the high street, but perhaps more than that, for me, it meant really getting into serious green territory. Until now, I had been involved in campaigning against environmental waste with the washable nappies, but organic cotton clothing was going to open up a new set of ethical issues for me and my customers.

Our organic cotton clothing is made at Assisi Garments, run by the Assisi Sisters of Mary Immaculate in India's textile centre near Tiripur, Tamil Nadu. Many people think that Fairtrade is simply about ensuring that workers have proper sanitation and tea breaks as well as a fair wage, and while these are tremendously important to keep people well, happy and working in a climate of respect, Assisi's social programme is an example of what is being done to help people out of poverty and to keep them there.

The Sisters have many schools and projects across India funded by the work they do in America, Germany and Holland, and in 1994, they were given a substantial donation from a couple who had spent their last days in one of the Sisters' old people's homes in Germany. Initially, a lot of their work had been with leprosy victims, but they were looking for new projects. Most of their funds were going towards deaf and mute children, as well as the very poor, and they

were looking at ways of reinvesting the money into new projects, particularly those that could offer training and employment to graduates from their schools.

The Sisters believe that textiles can provide a sustainable income through the factory to house, feed and train a small number from their boarding schools for disabled, mentally retarded, blind, deaf and mute children. The girls are at least 18 by the time they get to Assisi Garments, and as one of the big issues in textiles has always been child labour, it was a way in which they could ensure the minimum age.

Disabled girls and women in India are dealt a particularly rough lot, particularly if they are poor as well. At Assisi, many of them stay until they get married, and because they are so well trained and Assisi is so well regarded in the industry, they can go on to work in textiles for the rest of their lives if they want to. They are also given a substantial cash sum towards their marriage settlement, the dowry that is such a huge burden for poor parents in India. They would never have had these kinds of opportunities without the Sisters, because most of their families are terribly poor.

With regular clothing orders from us and others, Assisi is able to run production all year round – a much better position to be in than relying solely on seasonal fashion orders. As my business develops, Assisi continues to grow with the increased demand from my company and all of its other clients. Ten years on, the factory employs 200 people, 100 of them regular tailors and skilled labourers, and 100 young women who are housed there and fed by kitchen staff who are graduates of the Assisi schools. All the workers are given four breaks a day including lunch, which is cooked in the convent, and they all pile into the little chapel for prayers at 6 p.m. before the final shift.

Now the likes of Walmart, Tesco, M&S, Nike and H&M are knocking on their doors, as they step into the Fairtrade clothing business. If they do bring their orders to Assisi, the impact on the wider community will be enormous. Since 2000, a good school has been built as more skilled workers are attracted to the regular work at Assisi. The local hotel where all the buyers stay is now building new rooms for its increasingly large and demanding customer base, as well as a hall for marriages and other ceremonies for the local population. Because the factory has done so well, there's a great deal of interest from within the textile industry too, and there is a big trade fair each year now, which again brings money to town. And the guy selling tea on the lane outside the factory can't believe his luck!

The impact extends even further. The success of the factory has enabled the Sisters to secure an enormous loan to build a cancer hospital in Kerala. Twelve per cent of the local population there are affected, either personally or by having someone in their home that suffers from cancer. Ironically, it's the use of pesticides on crops that they believe is one of the most likely causes.

It's a story that I think sums up the whole issue of being a green parent; if we, as the world's richest consumers decide to buy an organic sleep suit rather than its synthetic cheap alternative, we are signing up to change the inequalities between the First and Third Worlds and help them out of poverty and disease. We are backing a new attitude of respect and responsibility in manufacturing by saying 'no' to the exploitation of workers in the cotton fields whose lives are threatened by the toxicity of the pesticides used there, and the damage to the wildlife and eco-system that they cause. We are insisting on Fairtrade conditions for the people whose work ensures that our babies sleep in breathable, chemical-free, super-soft material. With fewer pesticides in the cotton fields as the demand for organic clothing grows, we're helping to use less oil and reducing the global drain on a finite resource. Now, as you sit down with your (Fairtrade) cup of tea and put your baby shopping list together, just think how much of a difference you really can make to the future.

## key principles

- Reduce, recycle, refill and reuse

- Reduce your carbon footprint

- Use the car less, share rides and try asking your neighbours if they need anything when you go to the shops

- When buying a car consider a hybrid car or an electric car

- When buying a new dishwasher or washing machine, try and buy the most energy-efficient model

- Instead of washing powder, try eco balls, eco discs or aqua balls. Or try using nothing at all as most dirt will come out with warm water and the rotation of the washing machine

- Try not to tumble dry. If you do, use dryer balls which reduce the drying time

- Washing at 30°C (86°F) is usually good enough for most of your laundry

- Check out Greenpeace's list of the ingredients to avoid in your cleaning products

- Shower instead of bathing or use your bathwater for the garden with a Drought Buster siphon pump known as a Water Green

- Save water in your toilet cistern by installing a water-saving device

- Insulate the wall cavities and loft of your house and replace or repair draughty windows and doors

- Reduce water miles by using water-filter jugs instead of bottled water

- Donate unwanted goods to charity or recycle them

- Compost where you can or get a wormery

chapter two
## THE HEALTH OF YOUR BABY

# *your baby's health*

As a pregnant mother or as a new parent, the health of your
baby is going to quickly become your first concern. We might
have a preference for the sex of our child pre-birth, but when
it comes down to it, all that really matters is that he or she is
healthy. If you eat, drink and exercise properly during
pregnancy, most babies will come out ready to take on the
world.

Babies, like the planet they are born on, are pretty resilient
little things, as long as you treat them with respect but not
with caution or anxiety. It's a big mistake to treat them with kid
gloves; just watch the difference between how you and your
midwife pick up your newborn and you'll realize how robust
babies really are.

They tend to be pretty easy too; stick them on a breast and
off they go – most of the time anyway! You don't need me to
tell you that you need to be eating your five portions of fruit
and vegetables every day, and if you need any persuasion to
go organic, read Chapter 3. The healthier you are, the
healthier your baby will be, and if you can use the opportunity
to change some wasteful habits along the way, the changes
you make now really will change the world.

This chapter gives an overview of some of the baby health
issues that connect with being a greener parent. I'm not a
doctor or a baby health expert so I'm not presenting myself as
a guru on this subject but I believe there is good evidence
that natural is best for your baby's health and for the planet's.

# *your baby's immune system*

Your baby truly is an explosive little growth package. From pretty much the moment of his conception to the first two years after birth, his cells are developing at an incredible rate. In the uterus, cells are furiously busy over the nine months' gestation period multiplying and dividing into organs and tissues. We know that many critical stages of development happen in the womb including key genetic and hormonal changes that can determine the future health of major organs.

A new baby's immune system is like the foundations of a new home. Naturally strong, it still needs to be built with the best products if it is to support a new life and fight disease-producing organisms such as bacteria, viruses, fungi and parasites. Life is all about exposure to different viruses and bacteria, and just as muscles need building up to enable an adult to run fast enough to get out of danger, so a child's immune system is designed to actually strengthen and protect him as he grows up. Putting him in a sterile bubble won't help him at all; an immature immune system does not mean that it is weak but that it is delicate and worthy of a bit of respect.

The best time to build the first blocks of an immune system are way before birth, preferably before conception, although I'll admit that detoxing was the last thing on my mind at the time. There is overwhelming evidence that breastfeeding for at least six months will strengthen a baby's immune system, and weaken it if you don't.

Pollution in the environment and later, in food, will attack any immune system, so the stronger it is, the better it will deal with it. Smoking, drinking, even eating too many oranges according to Chinese medicine, can all have an effect on your unborn baby's developing immune system. The increasing incidences of eczema, hay fever, asthma and allergies in babies may well be linked to the amount of exposure we subject our bodies to while we're carrying them.

The immune system has got a lot of work to do, and feeding it pesticide-ridden vegetables and clothing its protective skin in synthetics won't give it the best start! Instead choose organic food and organic cotton clothing, which breathes naturally. The skin is the body's largest organ and 60 per cent of what it absorbs goes straight into the bloodstream. The residue of pesticides used in growing the food and cotton as well as any chemicals used in the manufacturing of his clothes will be easily absorbed and accumulate in his immature system.

The world our children's immune system is exposed to is quite different to the one we or our parents had to deal with. With so many chemicals now in our day-to-day lives, from our household cleaning products to our shampoo to our food, it is no wonder that some of them manage to find their way into our bodies. Tests have even found traces of these chemicals in the umbilical cords of newborn babies and mothers.

6 Experts say that currently we are exposed to 500 times more chemicals than our forefathers were in the 1940s. 9

## *your baby's digestive system*

A baby's digestive system is a work in progress and continues to develop throughout his first year of life. It's for that reason that health experts recommend breastfeeding for at least the first four months, preferably six. Even if parents have allergies themselves, breastfeeding can delay any possibility of a hereditary link.

By six months, he will let it be known, usually by grabbing your food out of your hand, that he's ready for solids. It's around this time that the digestive system is put under most stress as he begins to draw upon his energy reserves to start making his crucial first moves, lifting his head, beginning to sit up and move around for more of the day. Introducing new supplies is vital at this time, with baby rice or single vegetable and fruit purées the easiest for him to digest. Cow's milk and wheat are not advisable at this age.

This is the point when you decide what you're going to do with that hardy little digestive system; it's your choice to buy organic or pesticide-free fruit and vegetables or not, but the chemicals you'll be introducing into his tiny gut if you don't, will certainly have an effect. From conception until one year of age, a baby is at his most vulnerable, with cells multiplying at their peak and only a limited diet to draw upon. Add pesticides to his dinner by not buying organic fruit and vegetables, and you're asking a great deal more of his immune and digestive systems. Those pesticides will be absorbed more quickly in a baby's digestive system, which is much more efficient than that of an adult at absorbing nutrients – and anything else – in his foods. Adults can also eliminate more efficiently than a baby whose immature kidneys are not yet sufficiently developed to excrete harmful substances, which may then circulate in the body for longer. If the immune system is ready to take on life's natural germs in order to grow stronger, the digestive system does not need your help with man-made pollutants; the strain of trying to get rid of them will weaken it and put it under unnecessary stress.

## *the illness within*

The doctor should always be a call away, but how you view illness or weakness will change the more time you spend using naturopathic remedies. Conventional Western (allopathic) medicine is largely about quick fixes. The consequence is that you will probably never know what caused your illness in the first place and you'll speculate as to why you keep getting ill. It's certainly influenced by the power of the huge multinational pharmaceutical companies who deliver their latest research to over-worked doctors in the easiest ways to digest. On the other hand, naturopaths recognize that illness always comes from an imbalance in the body. You'll start to see how having a cold is an indicator of how healthy the body really is. More than two colds a year and the body is probably not working as well as it should to get rid of waste products that one good cold is designed to sort out through a streaming nose.

In a child, a snotty nose is not always a symptom of a cold, and could be something to do with a food disorder, often kicked off by a wheat allergy and aggravated by a diet of mucus-forming dairy products. Sedating a clingy or whiny child with some of the cold remedies on the market is just about the worst thing you can do. Eliminating the wheat and dairy from his diet will give you a much better insight into what's going on with your child. That old adage 'better out than in' is what the body seems to believe, so avoid all those preparations from the pharmacy if you want your baby to be left to get rid of it all naturally.

Suppressing a cold, or any sign that the body is having an internal fight, will give it a clear signal that you're not listening. We are so conditioned to keep our children from suffering that we often reach out for the bottle of medicine without thinking, but naturopaths believe that if you suppress those tell-tale signs that something needs to get out, the body will internalize the problem, believing that pushing it to the surface just doesn't work. There is a link between this kind of suppression and lung conditions, so if suppressed with a dose of medicine, a snotty nose could become a hacking cough or a more serious respiratory problem. Chinese medicine considers the skin to be the second lung, and if the body fails to get your attention through an eczema condition, that next step could mean an asthma attack.

Some problems might never be found without the kind of detective work complementary medicine employs. One of my customers told me about her newborn's dreadful colic, which she treated with gripe water and trips to the doctor. Nothing worked until she took her to a cranial osteopath who found her baby had a compression in her vertebra, a very common result of the birth process. She was amazed; the birth had been quick and very gentle, in water and the baby had seemed happy enough until ten weeks old when she began to howl day and night. The cranial osteopath explained that with her first growth spurt, what was a slight discomfort had become unbearable, causing tightness in her gut and digestive problems. A gentle manipulation sorted out the compression in a couple of minutes flat and she was right as rain again. Without intervention, that could have become a chronic back problem by the time she was in her twenties.

Osteopath and naturopath, Cissi Williams explains this particular cause of colic in her must-have book, *The Well-Being Handbook: An A–Z Guide to Holistic Healing* (see Resources).'Birth trauma, such as a quick or long labour, the use of forceps or ventouse, awkward birth position or lying head down for a long period before birth are possible causes (of colic). These factors increase the strain placed on the baby's head and body as it descends through the birth canal, and often the baby experiences pain and discomfort after the birth. This can lead to the compression of the nerve supplying the stomach as it exits from the area between the skull and the neck, as well as causing strain from the ribcage, thoracic spine, sacrum and the fascia in the gut.'

# natural birth

When I was about to give birth, I was like so many women I know who want to find a pill to help me deal with the unknown. Later I would listen in awe to the stories from customers who found pregnancy and childbirth the most empowering time of their lives, how they became aware of what their bodies were capable of, how miraculous birth really is and just how built for survival both mother and baby are. While they were at active birth classes and planning their water births, I was working full-time and eating out afterwards! It's just common sense really; what you put in, you get out is my business philosophy, but it seemed an alien idea to apply it to childbirth at that time.

## your holistic team

A good team around you will help you make the right decisions and support you through the early years. The names of local homeopaths and cranial osteopaths really should be added to your list of useful information, so important are they in strengthening your baby's natural reserves and dealing quickly and effectively with everyday issues such as birth trauma, digestive disorders and glue ear as your baby develops. Apparently over 90 per cent of babies suffer some kind of birth trauma, most of it requiring nothing more than a bit of ironing out by a cranial osteopath through skilful but gentle manipulation of the cranium and the skeletal structure so that the body's irrigation channels can pump away at their natural best. I remember customers telling me about babies who had been unable to breathe and feed at the same time which was hell for both mother and baby, another whose earache was so bad as she grew into her first year that she was almost hospitalized, and all cured by cranial osteopathy. Spend your pregnancy asking around for the best ones, or consult the General Osteopathic Council (see Resources).

A good homeopath will help you understand the unique nature of your baby's constitutional make-up – and be your best friend as you hurtle through the challenges that make childhood such a bumpy ride. Homeopathy is also fairly easy to use for common ailments. Many parents are worried about using something that they don't understand on their babies, but the great thing about homeopathy is that it can't do any harm. Babies aren't as sceptical as their parents might be; it either works or it doesn't. If you start using it during pregnancy, try the Helios homeopathic kits (see Resources) with full instructions for birth. They also produce first aid and travel kits that can be picked up in many good naturopathic health shops.

## *preparing for birth*

Many people come across naturopathic remedies when they are pregnant, either in order to make their pregnancy as healthy as possible or because they panic at the eleventh hour and think they need help! If they call on some of the many specialists found on the Internet or on the high street (see Resources), they may find a whole new attitude towards their own health, as well as ways to strengthen their baby's natural defences when the time comes.

New parents need all the help that they can get; in most cultures, it's unheard of for a woman to look after a newborn baby by herself, but we are proud and arrogant enough to think we can put our bodies through such an ordeal on our own. It's no wonder that we're ruining the planet!

## *mother and baby essentials*

For most babies, a good diet and a common-sense approach from their parents is enough to protect them, although anything you can naturally do to boost an immature gut and immune system will make things a lot easier for all of you as time ticks on.

Breastfeeding is undoubtedly the best way to ensure that your baby gets the full quota of nutrients, and as we all try to find ways of reducing our carbon footprint, watching a mother feeding a newborn is all we need to know; slow down, reuse, recycle. Researchers from the University of Toronto have even identified a new kind of protein in breast milk that helps jump-start a baby's immune system, providing active protection to the baby. The protein, called soluble CD14, works to develop B cells, which are immune cells that are instrumental in the production of antibodies.

Some women do find it incredibly difficult to breastfeed and resort to help from professionals. For others, it's not that he won't latch on in the first place, but that he develops an early preference for the bottle; often the reality of going back to work, expressing breast milk and having someone else feed your baby until you get home means that he might decide not to take the breast so readily. He doesn't have to suck as hard with the bottle to get to the good stuff, and the stress of persuading him to feed when you're tired is a common problem.

# food and milk production

**Foods to increase milk production**
- 3 x 10ml brewers yeast added to cereal
- Dill seeds
- Fennel seeds
- Fenugreek
- Turnip
- Peanuts
- Watercress
- Raspberries
- Alfalfa
- Nettles
- Milk thistle

**Foods to decrease milk production**
- Dried figs
- Lentils
- Basil
- Mint
- Sage

Anxiety can stop the milk flowing, as can a poor diet, which might be the by-product of your racing around trying to get everything done in the day. Julian Scott's excellent guide, *Natural Medicine for Children* (sadly now out of print, but order it from your library or find a second-hand copy on the web) lists foods that can increase your milk production (as well as those to decrease it). See the box opposite for the list. Whether your baby is being fed by breast or bottle, the cuddle he gets while he's having his dinner is also a huge boost to his wellbeing.

# herbal and homeopathic essentials

Herbal medicine and homeopathy are two of the most popular ways of tackling minor illnesses effectively. This is due to the fact that both tend to be easy to administer and parents would often rather seek a more natural means to cure childhood problems than resorting to antibiotics. Finding a reputable homeopath or herbalist is not difficult, please check out the Resources section.

## herbs

Herbs are particularly easy to give to a breastfed baby, either through the mother's milk, or as tinctures or teas in a bottle. Herbs such as elderberry, thyme and eyebright, with their anti-catarrh and anti-inflammatory properties, are an excellent herbal remedy for babies who are full of mucus and finding feeding difficult. Hyssop is an expectorant, and carminatives

# homeopathic essentials

Here are nine remedies that are suitable for minor problems:

- Belladonna for fever
- Arnica for bruising and shock
- Aconite for common colds
- Bryonia for mucus
- Chamomilla for teething (angry babies)
- Pulsatilla for teething (clingy babies)
- Hepar. Sulph for earache accompanied by sore throat
- Kali mur. for earache with thick phlegm
- Nat. mur for watery phlegm

Childhood diseases are nature's way of boosting the immune system. There are a number of homeopathic remedies to aid natural healing. Ask for x 30 potency:

- Chicken Pox – Rhus Tox
- Measles – Morbillinium
- Mumps – Phytolacca
- Whooping Cough – Pertussin

are great for the digestive system with anti-spasmodic properties. Peppermint, fennel, dill – these have all been passed down across the centuries for one reason: they work.

## homeopathy

Among the essentials in every household, arnica is generally useful for bruising (and excellent after birth) and shock. Aconite can help with anxiety, especially in labour when the adrenals may confuse the body and stop the birthing hormone, oxytocin, from working properly. Pulsatilla is a must-have remedy for clingy babies getting through teething or colic. Chamomilla is for the frustrated, angrier babies going through the same ordeal. See the list of homeopathic essentials in the box opposite.

## natural analgesics

Amber necklaces, I have been told, are given to every child at birth in Scandanavia and are increasingly popular in continental Europe. When they are worn, they act as a natural analgesic, so are great for headaches, toothaches, earaches and teething pains. They have even been used to help eczema and allergies. My customers rave about these necklaces. There's a testimonial from a man in my catalogue who came back to tell me how his daughter had lost hers and was getting really cranky. When they eventually found it down the back of the sofa and put it on her again, she was fine. People have said that they're dangerous, so I always say that they should be used under supervision. I took my baby's off when he went to nursery because you don't want other kids pulling it when it's around his neck. You just have to use your common sense.

## *antibiotics*

There may be times when antibiotics are essential in killing a bacterial infection and in some cases may even be life-saving. But they will always have long-term effects on the immune system and cannot restore the body's natural ability to fight off the bugs that are designed to keep it fighting fit. Live yogurt is an easy way to restore the good intestinal bacteria. Look for the acidophilus culture on the list of ingredients. Naturopaths will suggest that you treat the diarrhoea or whatever it was that you were given the antibiotics for in the first place.

Stripping a problem back to where it started is common sense in any other aspect of our lives, but the pharmaceutical industry has a stake in keeping us in the dark. Let's hope the green industry helps to redress the balance; the amount of chemicals our bodies eliminate into the water supply should be enough to turn up the heat sooner or later.

## *vaccinations*

Unbelievably, vaccinations at birth may soon be the norm. US scientists believe that they have stumbled across the molecular holy grail of neonatal immunology. Most vaccinations are given to babies at two months of age but

# Pasteur or Bechamp?

Louis Pasteur believed that disease comes from bugs, external to the body, which have to be fought off because they are implacable and can attack anyone. His theories have found historical favour, although they were largely plagiarized from Bechamp, and they led to germ theory and in turn to vaccination.

Antoine Bechamp believed that bacteria found in diseased people mutated within the person as a result of an unhealthy environment, that they are not the cause of disease but the result of it.

On this premise, Pasteur would argue that new drugs would be needed as more and more complex bacteria inhabit our world. Bechamp would argue that if a particular virus is responsible for a particular disease then it follows that everyone exposed to it will fall ill. But some people have an innate resistance even though they may have been exposed to the virus, so something else is at work.

The question is which scientist do you choose to believe when it comes to the vaccination debate?

they believe that this new drug could stimulate an immune response in newborns, following the discovery of a type of molecule present at birth.

For most of us, the vaccination debate is tricky. The media agenda falls heavily on the side of the pharmaceutical industry, which would have us believe that it is drugs rather than improved living conditions that are responsible for the decrease in childhood mortality. But there is a growing voice among parents who have watched their children develop eczema, allergies, autism and asthma after being vaccinated. The row is inconclusive, and there is no erring on the side of caution with this one. If you decide to have your child vaccinated, the smart advice is to wait until his immune system is better developed so that he can cope more effectively with the foreign antibodies that are intended to spur it into action.

# chemicals and your baby

Pregnancy and new parenthood is when adults are supposed to morph from irresponsible adolescence or 'middlescence' into the great protector, the grown-up. There are plenty of cultures that believe that there are three eras in each lifetime: the child, the grown-up and the elder, roughly apportioned into 30 years. Typically in the West, we tend to have a crisis with our mid-life, hanging on in there for as long as we can.

## illnesses affected by the environment

According to the Office for National Statistics' latest study (2004), 21 per cent of children aged 2 to 15 years were diagnosed with asthma in England; 24 per cent with eczema; and 9 per cent with hay fever. The number of new cases of asthma each year in the United Kingdom is six times higher than it was 25 years ago.

According to statistics in the USA, 8.9 per cent of children have asthma, 5.5 per cent have eczema and 10.5 per cent are reported as having hay fever. The prevalence of eczema worldwide in children is estimated to be 10 per cent. In Australia, 15.6 per cent of the population is estimated to have hay fever or allergic rhinitis.

Maybe that's why so many new parents go for the scary world of reports and doomsayers. I did spend my time at first wading through reports and websites about nappies and chemicals, and you may well do the same. There's the *Lancet* report by Philippe Grandjean and Philip Landrigan (Volume 368, Number 553, December 2006) on the link between neurodevelopment and chemicals and the Greenpeace report 'Cleaning up our Chemical Homes' by Madeleine Cobbing and edited by Martin Hojsik (published in 2003 and then updated by Greenpeace International in 2006), which are both suitably scary.

The World Wildlife Fund (WWF) spent the last five years campaigning to ensure that hazardous chemicals would be substituted with safer alternatives wherever possible through the new EU chemicals legislation, known as REACH (Registration, Evaluation and Authorization of Chemicals), which was published in December 2006. The WWF tested the blood of 400 individuals and the results showed that everyone was contaminated with a cocktail of persistent, bio-accumulative and toxic man-made chemicals.

But after what WWF calls an 'intense attack by the global chemicals industry' that 'weakened the final conclusions', the REACH report concluded the following: although chemicals that build up in living organisms and those that linger in the environment for a long time will have to be replaced whenever safer alternatives are available, we'll still be able to buy chemicals that WWF believes may cause cancer or birth defects, affect DNA or disturb the hormone system or cause other serious illnesses (so-called CMRs – carcinogens, mutagens or substances that are toxic to reproduction – and hormone-disrupting chemicals).

There are no definitive reports that link the massive increase of man-made chemicals in everyday use (500 a year at the last count) with ill health, but while scientists are finding residues of chemicals in breast milk and umbilical cords, you have to ask yourself how they got there. You only need to watch someone give up smoking with the help of a nicotine patch to know just how powerfully the skin absorbs whatever you put on it.

# eczema, asthma and hyperactivity

There is conclusive research that shows that a number of illnesses have increased as the result of environmental changes and the heavy use of chemicals in the world today. Amongst the most prevalent are eczema, asthma and hyperactivity.

## eczema

After months of dealing with my baby's skin issues, I realized that this was a good time to find out about alternatives to traditional medicine. Trying to stop my child from scratching was impossible at times, although the scratch mittens that I found for him did wonders. But it was the organic balms and

## cleanliness isn't next to godliness!

In the 1950s only 3 per cent of children suffered from eczema. Today it affects more than one in five and the numbers continue to rise. Although, as with asthma, the rise is likely to be due to a number of factors, Dr Michael Cork, consultant dermatologist at Sheffield University, believes he's pinpointed a key issue. Dr. Cork has shown that over the past 30 to 40 years in the UK there has been a dramatic rise in bathing and the corresponding use of bubble baths and bath gels.

Spending on these products has almost doubled in the last 20 years. Bath gels and bubble baths contain surfactants, chemicals that act as foaming agents. Surfactants can break down the fats in skin cells that help them retain water; so gels can dry out the skin, decrease its integrity and cause irritation.

pure cotton nappies and clothing that calmed his itching and cooled his skin that made me wonder how I could have considered opting for the first medicines that my doctor gave me. I still call the doctor when I need to, but it's no longer the knee-jerk response it used to be. Babies don't need half the chemicals we throw at them out of ignorance and panic, and neither does the planet.

Eczema is, along with a temperature or a rash, a clue that something is not right in the body's engine room, the immune system. The skin is the protective barrier to the body and its largest organ, working day and night to keep the bad (foreign organisms) out and the good (water) in. Eczema is what happens when the water escapes, leaving the skin itchy and so dry that it flakes and can become inflamed. For a child, it's almost as unbearable as it is for the parents trying to keep their baby from suffering. Along with asthma and hay fever, eczema is the most common chronic childhood disease.

Experts, led by scientists at the University of Dundee, say that they have discovered the gene that causes the dry, scaly skin and predisposes individuals to atopic dermatitis, or eczema as it's more commonly known. Margaret Cox, Chief Executive of the National Eczema Society, said: 'To discover that eczema patients don't have the gene which should protect the skin by keeping water in and keeping foreign organisms out is a real step forward.' Apparently, this gene produces a protein called filaggrin that is normally found in large quantities in the outermost layers of the skin, but mutates in some people allowing foreign substances to easily enter the skin and affect the immune system. This might prove useful information to take to a doctor and might pave the way for revolutionary treatment for eczema in the future, but most complementary therapists would agree that it's the immune system that is the key to understanding eczema, and the answer won't be to simply slap a cream on it.

## asthma

Asthma is a chronic, incurable, disease that inflames the airways and lungs, causing an alarming shortness of breath and wheezing, sometimes for as much as a couple of hours. In some extreme cases, it can even lead to death. The airways constrict and asthmatics compare an attack to breathing through a straw. They fight for breath, which causes serious stress on the body, the spirit and on those attempting to help. Obviously, the doctor is the first call when you hear your baby wheezing badly, but parents who tell me about their terrifying experiences with an asthmatic child say that it really helps to keep calm, whispering soothing words while help is on its way.

## off-gassing or out-gassing

An Australian study published in 2004 linked asthma with volatile chemicals in household products. Volatile chemicals such as those found in many man-made products such as plastic or nylon, tend to 'off-gas' or release a gas into the environment. These gases aren't generally a problem in well-ventilated homes and workplaces but they can have a negative effect if collected in a closed room with a lack of fresh air.

Asthma attacks tend to set off by a specific set of irritants and allergens, such as cigarette smoke, dust mites and air pollution, so check to see what you can do in your own home. Colds, food additives and stress can trigger attacks in weak-lunged children. It is often hereditary; if anyone in your family has had tuberculosis or suffers from eczema or hay fever, even more reason to cut out the external pollutants.

Researchers pull both ways on the link with exercise; on the one hand, kids are more susceptible to air pollution simply because they tend to spend more time outside. The longer they are running around, breathing at a higher rate relative to body weight than the average adult, the longer they are exposed to air pollutants. But some scientists who believe that genetic traits change far too slowly to account for the recent increase in asthma cases, suggest that it's because children are spending more time indoors, increasing their exposure to certain allergens and indoor air pollutants.

A study by Bristol University of more than 7,000 children undertaken in Britain in 2004 found that children born into households that are high users of products such as bleach, disinfectant and cleaning fluids are twice as likely to suffer persistent wheezing.

It seems that asthmatic kids can't win. But although it can't be cured, asthma can be controlled with treatment, either medical or complementary such as homeopathy and cranial osteopathy, and environmental interventions such as those laid out in Chapter 4. If your baby is yet to be born, reduce the stress in your life, eat well and make sure that you breast-feed as long as possible; a study in 2000 of more than 5,000 children in Brazil revealed that breastfeeding seems to protect kids from asthma and wheezing, although as they had no family history of asthma, the study could not be considered conclusive.

## hyperactivity and ADHD

Understanding more about the way the body works will also help you put some of the scary facts that you will find in this book into the right context. Hyperactivity and ADHD for example are conditions that the anti-chemical lobbyists will claim as their own, and there is plenty of evidence to suggest that food additives, nutritional deficiencies and phosphates in canned foods can have an influence on certain children. But there may be a deeper-seated reason for this disease, stemming again from birth itself and a cranial osteopath is your first port of call. Understanding that birth is always an incredibly stressful experience for both baby and mother and can result in your baby developing a highly charged central nervous system, will help you think more holistically about the whole thing. A calm birth environment is a good start for any baby, but if you suspect you have a hyperactive baby, a 'baby swim' can help him to sleep properly. Getting an older child to do some really strenuous exercise will allow excess adrenaline to kick into touch all the other over-active hormones that his central nervous system is firing left, right and centre.

Some babies are born with hypersensitivity and will suffer from conditions that other kids easily fend off. A lot of my customers find their way to Green Baby in the first place because of these conditions and most decide to change the way that they live, swapping poor diets for fresher, organic foods, and ripping up old carpets that they reckon are responsible for mite allergies to create more space and light in their lives. Both types of asthma, extrinsic (allergy-induced reactions to outside influences such as pollen and mites) and intrinsic (bronchial reactions triggered by colds, stress, pollutants etc) are supposed to be due to hypersensitivity.

## *avoiding chemicals*

But there's little point in being negative when the options that are healthier for both your baby and the planet are so much nicer to have around. You're going to save a fortune on the supermarket shop when you learn how to buy less and recycle more. You will realize, if you don't already, that healthy growth is about preparing the soil, avoiding a reliance on chemicals and nurturing it with good food and plenty of liquid. Concentrating on what you can do to help your child grow healthily rather than fighting off invisible demons is about getting it all into perspective. Make choices now based on health rather than fear and your child will absorb that more easily than a cocktail of chemicals on his nursery wall.

I've decided that the world is not the poisonous place that I thought it was in the first flush of baby blues and new-parent paranoia. But I still see that fear all the time in other mothers; I remember taking my then two-year-old to see a friend and her new baby in the maternity ward of a large London hospital and being told that we couldn't come in as children carry too many germs! My friend poked her head out of the door to apologize. 'He hasn't been vaccinated yet!' she hissed!

'Against what?' I asked in amazement. She didn't know that we don't vaccinate newborns, but fresh out of the delivery room, she was already brainwashed to believe that she should protect her baby from the world outside.

There are some very simple things you can do to minimize any potential risks to your baby and these are all explained in detail in the following chapters. Lay the groundwork for a healthy baby with an organic diet for you and him, regular exercise and keep an eye on your stress levels. Spend some time looking at the contents of your bathroom cabinet and cleaning agents under the sink, and where you can, replace them with more environmentally friendly options and reduce your usage. As you're bound to redecorate the nursery ready for your new arrival, give some thought to the most natural environment you can create (Chapter 4 provides all the details). Following these simple precautions will help ensure your baby's immediate world is as natural and green as it can be.

Most importantly perhaps, tapping into the magic of natural medicine helps you to see more clearly what your child is made of. Reaching for the phone to call the doctor or rummaging in the medicine cabinet to see what might put him to sleep for a bit is not generally the answer. Most childcare issues are easily solved with time to listen; even the tiniest baby can tell you what he needs if you tune in enough. But maybe it's the way that you begin to trust yourself to deal with the everyday ailments that is the most important thing that natural medicine can offer you.

# key principles

As a new mother you are likely to be quite overawed by all the paraphernalia that comes with your baby and you will be bombarded with helpful advice. If you observe the philosophy in this opening chapter, you won't go far wrong:

- Reduce the stress in your life and eat at least five portions of fruit and vegetables a day. This is good for the health of both you and your baby

- Think before you expose your baby to the numerous chemicals that are found in clothes other than organic cotton

- Feed your baby organically; it will help his digestion

- Avoid using bath gels and bubble baths that contain surfactants, chemicals that act as foaming agents

- Avoid extensive use of products such as bleach, disinfectant and cleaning fluid

- Check to see what you can do in your home to reduce irritants and allergens, such as cigarette smoke, dust mites and air pollution

- Make sure that you breastfeed as long as possible to boost your baby's immune system

- Find a cranial osteopath if your baby's birth was traumatic for him

- Try taking your baby for a swim if he is hyperactive

- Treat your child's problem naturally with homeopathic or herbal remedies first before resorting to antibiotics

- Always consult a doctor if your child has a temperature of 40 degrees or over, becomes vague or limp or loses consciousness, starts to twitch or feels cold on one side and hot on the other

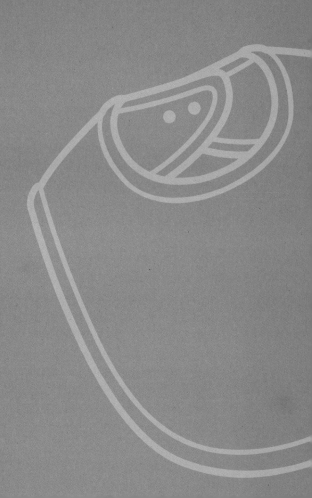

# chapter three

# FOOD AND HEALTH

# eating your greens

Food and the earth; it must be the most obviously symbiotic
relationship in the whole of this book. On the one hand, junk
food leads to a junk planet packed with people who dump on
their immune system in the same way that they happily dump
on a landfill. On the other, organic food, properly sourced
under Fairtrade conditions if from the developing world and
properly priced if locally grown, is as good for us as it is for
the planet. Just imagine how good it is then for your baby, not
just for his growing body, but for his healthy brain function
and immune system.

That old adage, 'you are what you eat' started to become
scary as the link strengthened between food and behaviour.
New parents started to read up on the latest research on the
link between allergies and nutrition. Lizzie Vann at Organix,
amongst others, wrote and commissioned studies on what we
were eating and what we were feeding our children, which led
to a mass of information (much of which is available on the
Organix website – see Resources). As a result, new parents
began to shop in a different way, reading ingredient lists,
buying organic, and when research showed that more than half
of all jarred baby food was now coming from organic sources,
they bought those too. We didn't just have information about
gluten being inappropriate for our babies, we had gluten-free
organic baby food in a jar. How easy was that?

Suddenly everyone was an expert, swapping stories about the
best ways to boost the immune system, debating the cost of
organic food and insisting that they avoided sugars and
processed products. A flurry of new evidence was coming out

of the science labs to prove that chemicals do indeed accumulate in our blood, breast milk, organs and tissues. The knowledge that bio-accumulative, persistent, hormone-disrupting chemicals could build up in our bodies and our *tiny babies'* bodies as we weaned them on to a pesticide-ridden diet was appalling. The truth is simple; breastfeeding as well as eating organically and avoiding sugars and processed foods are proven to be the best immune boosters.

Friends of the Earth (FOE) found that many fruit and vegetables carry residues of pesticides (known as persistent), and very often more than one at a time. Certain pesticides were found to have endocrine-disrupting properties, which affect the glands and the hormones, while others have the potential to affect the immune or nervous systems. Pesticide use is regulated, but the residue limits set are not necessarily 'safe' or may be exceeded, something that FOE is fighting to rectify.

# *allergies*

Links between the food we eat and allergies, eczema, hay fever, asthma and hyperactivity are now becoming mainstream as evidence is gathered from all over the world. My belief is that eating good organic food deals with most of the food issues you read about in the newspapers, but for kids who have endless allergies, skin and lung conditions there is a lot of new information filtering in from the scientific community.

One of the allergies that is becoming quite commonplace is an allergy to nuts. In the UK, US, Australia and Canada, the allergy has doubled in the past ten years and now affects one in 70 primary school children. One of the issues scientists will be looking at is whether or not peanut protein extract, which is used to make formula milk creamier, is the reason why so many children in the West are quietly developing nut allergies long before they show symptoms, and before anyone would dream of giving it to them in dilute form such as peanut butter. The LEAP (Learning Early About Peanut Allergy) study at London's St Thomas' Hospital will be studying this further with 480 babies aged between four and 11 months who already have eczema or an egg allergy as part of a randomized, controlled seven-year study.

## peanut puzzle

Current international guidelines recommend the avoidance of peanuts during pregnancy, breast-feeding and for the first three years of childhood, yet children in Africa, Asia and China, who snack on peanuts from a very early age have lower rates of peanut allergy than in the West.

# additives and preservatives

Food additives have been used by mankind for centuries. Salt, sugar and vinegar were among the first additives used to preserve food. In recent years, however, with the arrival of processed foods, there has been an increasing reliance on adding chemicals to preserve foodstuffs. Since 1987 Australia has had a system of labelling additives with a name or number and Europe has followed suit, with the so-called 'E' numbers, some of which are considered perfectly safe but some are known to be toxic.

There has been a lot of research in recent years regarding the link between nutrition and children's health. Specifically we know that nutrients like zinc, magnesium and omega 3 in fish oils and flaxseed are vital for healthy brain function and development and we are only too aware of the limitations of highly processed foods. What is of special interest to me is the evidence of the negative effects of all the 'unnatural' stuff we add to our food.

We know now that additives in our food, such as preservatives and artificial flavourings, can cause hormone and chemical disruptions in children and could lead to a number of physical or mental disorders, the most common being hyperactivity. Depriving your children of proper nutrients like zinc, magnesium and omega 3 in fish or flaxseed oils in their diet could mean that they struggle when they get to the classroom. If a child is prone to respiratory illnesses, additives could trigger even an asthmatic condition.

Food preservatives in use today can be divided into three

main groups: cosmetics, preservatives and processing aids, presently totalling about 3,794 different additives: 3,640 are used purely as cosmetics, 63 as preservatives and 91 as processing aids.

Foresight, a charity established in the United Kingdom in 1978, promotes the importance of good health and nutrition in both parents before conceiving a baby. The charity has produced a leaflet showing that the use of food additives has increased in the past thirty years and now totals over 200,000 tonnes per year. It is therefore estimated that an average person will consume 3.5–4.5 kg (8–10 lb) of food additives per year.

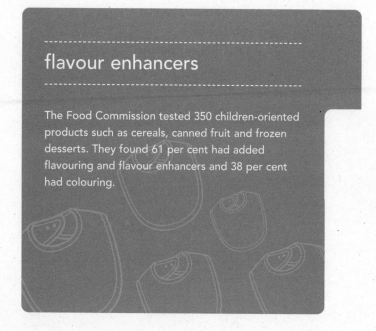

## flavour enhancers

The Food Commission tested 350 children-oriented products such as cereals, canned fruit and frozen desserts. They found 61 per cent had added flavouring and flavour enhancers and 38 per cent had colouring.

# changing the family diet

I didn't think much about the way I fed myself before I had my baby. Even when I was pregnant, I can't say that I changed my diet, except for avoiding alcohol. But I sure as hell changed my mind when my baby needed to move on to solids. Nothing was going to get into his stomach before I had checked and double-checked every ingredient in that jar. I didn't know about immune systems at the time, but I cooked like I had never cooked before and all so my kid had the best start. I eventually worked out that feeding the whole family well would also mean not polluting the planet.

The whole family turned organic overnight. I don't think I gave much of a thought to what organic meant for the environment. Jonathan Porritt, founder director of Forum for the Future and chairman of the UK Sustainable Development Commission wrote recently in *The Guardian* in January 2007, 'The climate change "gain" of buying organic is all but indisputable' but at the time, I had no idea that organic farming used up about 15 per cent less energy to produce the same amount of inorganic food. I would simply read the ingredients on the jars I bought in the supermarket. If I didn't understand them, I didn't buy them.

Jonathan and I enjoyed shopping at the local fishmonger, greengrocer and butcher at weekends, and later at the farmers' markets that have spread throughout London like a rash in the last couple of years. We avoided using the car by using public transport; living in the middle of London helped enormously of course. But we became aware of how much we relied on oil to get our food to us when the fuel protests of 2000 brought London to within three days of running out of food. Vegetable box deliveries still weren't really available and supermarket deliveries were in their infancy.

We still used the supermarket; Jonathan would check out all the labels, bringing new green products up to the trolley and showing me all the things he had found without 'E' numbers. Supermarkets were just beginning to stock organic baby products whose recipes we could either copy, or which we could stock up on for when we were hard-pushed. Jonathan and I ordered our vegetable box as soon as they became available, and found endless ways of adding omega 3 to Thomas' carrot puree without him spitting it out. We found, by trial and error, that avocados, sunflower and sesame seeds are excellent sources of omega 3 and 6, and flaxseed oil is tasteless.

# *why buy organic?*

All of the above just persuades me that organic really is best. If you need further persuasion, look at the Friends of the Earth or Soil Association information about pesticides (see Resources). According to FOE, about half of all British fruit and vegetables contain pesticides. As I said before, many of these are only used to make the fruit and vegetables more cosmetically perfect on the shelves. And did you know that removing pesticides from our polluted drinking water costs the United Kingdom £120 million ($237,059,982) per year?

The first real myth I need to dispel is about the expense of eating organic. It has long been assumed that organic food was beyond the pockets of most of us but in February 2007, *Which?* magazine researchers compared 11 products from organic, non-organic and own-brand ranges from the top five supermarkets. They found that choosing organic food over non-organic adds, on average, £5 ($9.87) to the cost. When compared with supermarket economy items, this rises to an extra £10 ($19.75). For many of us this is probably a revelation.

But it was when I started selling organic cotton clothing that I began to understand so much more about the supply chain, and to realize that organic food is not just about being the best source of nutrition for my family and the healthy biodiversity of the land, but that there's a whole other story going on. Once I had visited the cotton farmers in India and saw what it would take for them to diversify into soya for example, I realized the enormous impact of pesticides on the entire food chain.

Organic farming is not just about cleaning the soil; it's also about using less energy. These days, the Soil Association, which for 30 years was just an organization of organic farmers, giving advice and certification on organic soil standards, is leading the debate about climate change. Those

> **The huge growth in sales of organic food is testimony to the fact that people will make greener choices if we give them the right information, opportunity and incentive.**
>
> Sir Terry Leahy, Chairman of Tesco

who once thought that organic food was for do-gooders, now see that food is critical to greening up our lives.

Initiatives are slowly spreading across the world. One of Jamie Oliver's mentors, Alice Waters, the queen of cuisine in California, is behind the Edible School Yard project just outside San Francisco. Children have been growing their own organic food in the school yards there for the last ten years, and Alice is planning to roll it out across the USA. She says; 'If food became part of the curriculum, people would think differently about it. A new generation would grow up looking after the country in a different way. We're talking about food as a core curriculum in school where they would get grades and it would be part of academia. Every child needs to be involved and food should become an academic subject so that kids learn to participate. Gardens should become labs. The eco-gastro scene should be something that they should study. It opens up people's minds.'

Similarly, New Zealand has just announced that it plans to become the first organic country, and California's Marin

## transition

Mother Nature won't be hurried, and it takes time for soil to become clean again. Even the supermarkets are supporting a new generation of 'transition farmers' who are in the process of getting their organic certification.

Waitrose's Farmers Select label means that those goods are produced according to organic standards but have yet to be credited. It raises awareness among the consumers that farmers have to invest in a considerable period of time to get accreditation and unless their customers support them, it's financial suicide, however much they may want to contribute to environmental change and better health.

The consumer in turn realizes that they have to pay a higher price because of the additional costs the farmer must incur to convert to organic. So many people criticize the price of organic produce without thinking about what it takes for the farmers to supply the supermarkets. It's all about raising the level of understanding.

County is aiming at becoming 'the first all-organic county in America, a county in which residents and eaters recognize their mutual interdependence', according to Helge Hellberg, Executive Director of Marin Organic. Farmers are working with Marin Organic's distribution service to make use of every vegetable grown in organic soil, with 90 per cent of it going to the local schools. Any produce that the supermarkets reject as being the 'wrong' shapes and colours are then packed up and sent off to those who most need it, in hospitals, schools and prisons, while the rest are sold in vegetable boxes. Kitchen staff accompany students from the county's schools on trips to the farms to see where their food comes from. 'Everything comes back to the soil' said Hellberg. 'A one-hour trip can be a life changing experience for many of them, and they come back to school in love with food.'

In Oakland, California, residents plan to produce 30 per cent of their own food within the city boundaries by 2020 under a new initiative called Transition Towns. In the United Kingdom, similar community-level responses are underway in among others, Totnes and Lewes. Adrienne Campbell of the Lewes initiative told me that a lot of people are so terrified of climate change that they freeze rather than change their habits. The term 'transition' is meant to encourage people to take the time to think about what their new life will look like, to work with like-minds, to read up and plan, ready for a new way of living.

# local or global?

We also need to start thinking about whether we are a local or a global community. After years of buying meat from shrink-wrapped trays and strawberries in January, we finally have a picture in our minds of the farmer who produces our food. We understand how hard he works and the risks he takes when he becomes organic, but does he come from Kent or Kenya? Peak Oil is now pushing the debate towards ticking the local box. The Soil Association recently announced that it will be publishing a consultation paper outlining options ranging from labelling produce and carbon offsetting to an outright ban on air-freighting. Air-freighted food, which is mainly fresh fruit and vegetables, accounts for 0.1 per cent of total food miles and generates 13 per cent of total food transport carbon dioxide emissions, according to the Department for Environment, Food and Rural Affairs.

The 'buy local' lobby would probably say that all those green beans and soya products should be sold to the local population in the first place, but to me, it's a tricky argument. As it is flown to the export market as freight on passenger planes, you have to remember that many of those planes are flying anyway. If you don't buy the soya, you're jeopardizing the work of those farmers. We have to support these international markets. You have to realize that there's a person behind the produce. By buying that soya, you're putting money back into the environment and developing it. But Vandana Shiva, the environmentalist author, said at the Soil Association conference this year, that we shouldn't be too concerned about supporting small farmers in Kenya and their air-freighted green beans. 'As soon as it becomes big business, they get thrown off their land and are lucky if they get offered jobs at low wages to work as labourers.'

There are schemes already in place that support the workers such as the Blue Skies co-operative in Ghana, which grows organic pineapples, picks them at the peak of ripeness and then packs them and flies them to the UK. Zameen Organics in India, which protects the interest of organic farmers across the sub-continent does the same. Looking at the label can help you make the decision as to whether to buy or not.

# *eating as a family*

Eating around the table is a rare thing these days, with parents coming home at different times of the day; the childminder or the nursery may well be feeding your child five days out of seven in a couple of year's time. And if the adults there are too busy feeding small children, your kid is going to learn to eat what his neighbour is eating. By the time he's at school, you can forget it!

Eating well is not just about where the food comes from. Good health comes from eating chemical-free, natural foods together as a family. And when you're considering the local or global argument round the dinner table, consider how your ancestors have eaten for millions of years. Most cultures still feed their babies the food of their tribe, food from their own land.

Babies are genetically programmed to eat what you're eating. To them, food is a potential poison, but if Mum and Dad are eating it, it must be all right. According to Dr Gill Harris from the School of Psychology at the University of Birmingham in an article in *Junior Pregnancy and Baby Magazine*, 'The parent would have chewed it first, which is not to be recommended these days, but the child would know that the food was safe. In this way, "Primitive Baby" would have understood what to expect in terms of taste, texture and appearance, the essential three stages that they need to recognize before happily tucking in.'

## *learning taste*

'Children are born either liking all three tastes; sour, sweet and salt, or just the sweet,' says Dr Harris. 'The earlier you give a baby who likes just the sweet taste all three, the more likely she is to accept them. You also get their sense of smell going because smell and taste are more or less the same thing. That means that the child is better prepared for the foods that you are eating as a family.'

From anecdotal evidence from babies up to four months old, Dr Harris believes that younger babies do show a preference for salt, sweet or bitter tastes. 'It seems that the longer that you delay the introduction of solids, the more likely babies are to go for a sweet taste and the more resistant they become to new tastes.' Getting them interested in a range of tastes by six months is a good way to avoid faddy eating.

# consumer fear

There are so many anxieties around parenting these days, and the food industry is guilty of milking that. Parents panic about doing the right thing. I feel really silly now when I think about how little I used to think things through. I remember going for a meeting with the midwife at a London hospital where I was about to launch a big campaign to promote washable nappies and save the environment, and yet I was putting ready-made formula into a bottle for Thomas. I remember her looking at me as if I was mad. Why couldn't I have just prepared a bottle of my own milk? I suppose I believed that it might go off. Now you realize how stupid that is, how it makes you paranoid. But it's that consumer fear that makes a lot of money for the baby industry.

It's worse in some parts of the United States; you can even buy water that is supposed to be especially for formula. How paranoid do you have to be to buy that? I remember somebody trying to persuade me to sell ready-sterilized plastic throwaway bottles. I was puzzled as to why on earth you would need to throw away a bottle after you've fed a baby. She said it was unhygienic! This is what prompted me to look into food and drink containers and the healthy alternatives that might be available.

# hormone disruptors

As recently as 2005, the World Wildlife Fund (WWF) Chemicals and Health campaign, which tested the blood of 155 people in the UK across three generations found that Bisphenol-A (BPA), which is used to manufacture the polycarbonate plastic in baby feeding bottles, refillable water bottles and food containers is another hormone disruptor, mimicking the action of oestrogen in the body. They also found that phthalates can leach from plastic packaging and plastic food containers into fatty foods such as meat and dairy products, and have been regularly found in human blood and breast milk.

# the truth about food and drink containers

So we've all become focused on the food that we give our children, but how many of us are giving a thought to the food containers we use? It's extraordinary, but mine is still about the only company selling glass feeding bottles in the United Kingdom. A report by Greenpeace came out the year I was setting up my business, which concluded that the modern invention of plastic bottles contained phthalates and that these were potential hormone disruptors. They looked in particular at the standard baby feeding bottle and found that these phthalates had the potential to leach from the bottle into the ingredients.

Glass feeding bottles had gone out of style years ago so finding alternatives was not the easiest thing for parents to do. I sourced some from Germany and started selling them and they were amazingly successful. We were covered in the media, even in magazines at the time that you would never think would look at environmentally friendly products. But the idea of chemicals leaching into innocent babies' milk was enough to create a whole new product line! Since this report, feeding-bottle companies are very careful about the plastic they use. As long as bottles are thrown away when they start to show signs of wear or when they are scratched they should be fine.

Once again, it's not just what it's doing to our systems, but what plastic packaging is doing to the planet. Not all councils recycle plastic bottles and if you're throwing them away as soon as they get scratched, that's a hell of a lot of unnecessary waste going to the landfill. Glass is long lasting, doesn't scratch leaving places to harbour bacteria and it doesn't hold odours. It can be passed down to others and when it breaks, you simply put it out for recycling.

# nickel

Children who use stainless steel cutlery could develop allergies to nickel, even if it doesn't necessarily happen right away and it could be a contributory factor to the development of eczema. In addition to the potential health issues, ecologically the mining of nickel is far from good. Nickel uses a process in which large quantities of acid separate it from cobalt and mined ore. This 'pressure acid leach mining' is thought to be about to destroy the biodiversity of the land, but could be a potential environmental disaster. The process is new in nickel mining, but environmentalists remember when the process was used in gold mining in Colorado. The waste was not properly stored, and a huge explosion in 1993 burst one of the storage lagoons sending a torrent of acid into the Alamosa River, poisoning 17 miles of water and putting drinking supplies and crops at risk. The impact on the local economy lasted for years.

This was a whole new world that I was discovering. The more I found out, the more questions I had to ask. I was trying to strike a balance between what was truly scary and what I could live with, but I loved being an eco-detective; there is so much about the way we consume that doesn't make sense to me. It turns out that everything I discovered wasn't just best for baby but was also best for the planet. The green movement is all about asking questions, and that is what I hope I can encourage you to do too.

# a vision for the future

Mother Nature is a canny old bird, isn't she? All these scares, including the really big one, climate change, are probably her way of shaking our civilization out of its complacency and into a healthier stage of development. If Peak Oil means eating local again, it might even produce a bumper crop of allergy free super-babies, reared on food from their own organic soil and eaten in season. Asthma, eczema and hay fever might be subjects taught in history as classic symptoms of 'The Chemical Civilization'.

And you know what? We're not so far off; a report from the Department for Environment, Food and Rural Affairs produced in January 2007, found that people in the UK are buying more fruit and vegetables than we have done in the last 20 years. Household expenditure rose for cheese, eggs and milk, with a continuing switch from whole milk to semi-skimmed milk. There was even an increase in intake of fibre. We are also buying less confectionery and soft drinks; even sales of alcoholic drinks, both for the household and in pubs and restaurants, have gone down! We might yet turn into a super-breed strong enough to deal with the onslaught of the effects of climate change!

We're doing better
than we think we are.
Most people say that they
haven't got time to go
shopping, but it's our most
popular occupation. People say
that they want a one-stop shop, but they
love the experience of shopping. Put them in a shopping mall
and they're really happy, but look at the growth of farmers'
markets and tell me that people don't love to touch, look,
smell and talk about what they're buying from people who
have grown it themselves.

The day will come when the supermarkets will buy their
produce on a Fairtrade basis, working with the Third World
rather than exploiting and controlling it, and encouraging
transition farming with initiatives like Waitrose's Farm Select.
We'll buy our dry goods online from them and have them
delivered in a van that distributes to all our neighbours, using
one petrol tank rather than hundreds for the same journey.

We'll buy our local produce from a box scheme so that local
farmers have a sustainable market and can bank on going
organic if they haven't already. We'll buy fish from fishmongers
and meat from butchers, and they will all source locally. Local

money will be ploughed back into the local community. Everything that goes around really will come around!

Our lifestyle will become cheaper but only if we get out of the habit of throwing things away if we don't like them or don't know what to do with them. Most people in the First World are spoilt for choice, and one of the reasons that they don't buy a vegetable box regularly will be because they don't like something in it.

Is my vision realistic? Albert Einstein said 'Great Spirits have always encountered violent opposition from mediocre minds,' so we just have to put it out there; to quote another visionary book, the *Dhammapada*, a buddhist scripture, 'We are what we think. All that we are arises with our thoughts. With our thoughts we make our world. Speak or act with a pure mind and happiness will follow you as your shadow unshakeable.'

## key principles

There are number of good habits you can adopt and bad ones you can let go of, to ensure the health of you and your baby:

- Boost your baby's immune system by breastfeeding and avoiding processed foods

- Avoid refined carbohydrates such as white flour and white sugar

- Eat whole grains and plenty of fruit and vegetables, organic where possible

- Introduce zinc, magnesium and omega 3 fish oils into your child's diet to boost intelligence and brain power

- Invest in organic farming, which is energy saving

- Avoid preservatives and artificial flavourings, which can cause hormone

and chemical disruptions in children
and could lead to hyperactivity

- Avoid using plastic bottles or buying
  goods in plastic packaging because they
  can leach phthalates into the contents

- Throw away plastic bottles if they start to
  show signs of wear

- Don't let food come into contact with
  PVC film

- If your local council doesn't recycle
  plastic, ask why not

- Don't delay introducing your child to
  solids or he may develop a sweet tooth

# chapter four

# GREENING THE NURSERY

# how green is your home?

It may be when you're faced with a brand-new life coming into your own that you really look at the way you live for the first time. Until now, you may have dismissed a lot of those media claims that the amount of electricity we generate around us may harm us, that the electro-magnetic frequencies (EMFs) produced by electronic devices from the laptop to the washing machine may really be harmful. Some studies even suggest that there may be a link between EMFs and childhood cancers. With your tiny baby gurgling contentedly in the middle of those airwaves, you may think differently. And it may extend to a lot more than your personal computers.

## how to tackle EMF

While the scientists battle it out among themselves as to how to tackle this problem, there are some easy precautions that we parents can take:

- Try and limit the time that children spend in front of the computer to limit their exposure to EMFs.

- Unplug appliances that are not in use. This will also save energy as electrical devices continue to conduct electricity even on standby.

- Limit the number of electrical appliances in the nursery.

# eco-products

Kitting out a green nursery, or even detoxing your whole house in preparation for a new baby, is getting easier these days. I wanted Green Baby to be as green as we could be. It would be who we are, our brand, our USP (Unique Selling Point/Proposition). Journalists always ask 'Well, if you're so green, is this table environmentally friendly?' always expecting me to admit that it isn't, but it's important to me that it is. I spend a lot of time trying to find organic paints, green(ish) shelving and furniture that isn't sprayed with fire retardants or exuding poisonous glue fumes. As research accumulates to show the impact on the climate of opening a tin of paint, you would have to be pretty hard nosed to ignore the facts and pick up any old tin of paint.

Paints, varnishes, strippers and wood are the kind of thing that most people wouldn't think twice about until very recently. We might religiously buy natural household cleaning products but the truth is that detergents don't even make the scale compared with most DIY products. Follow this mantra: if you can't eat it, then don't breathe it in. Where paint is concerned, it's the volatile organic compounds (VOCs) that you need to be aware of. They produce ground-level ozone, which will increase your carbon footprint, and when you've finished painting, disposing of the paint is also particularly tricky as the chemicals can never fully degrade, increasing the carbon footprint yet again.

Now that I'm greening up my new home six years on, there are so many more products on the market. If green-DIY in the past involved getting a second mortgage, these days media pressure and consumer power have finally combined with a new generation of socially responsible management teams to inspire brand-new initiatives in retail, and DIY is one of them. You can't help feeling a little sceptical about the motivations and reality of their claims, but if large DIY chains remind their customers that there are people behind every product they sell with 'life-stories', hats off to them.

Being green is about understanding the supply chain; where the raw materials come from, how they are manufactured, under what kind of conditions, how they are transported to us and how they will be disposed. That means that you're protecting the earth and the people who live on it. One just doesn't work without the other in the long term. So maybe the large DIY chains recognize this as 'added value' to their products, and it gives them not just brownie points but awards and press coverage, but if that's their just rewards for cranking up awareness, let them have it. If it makes the paint cheaper, we can have it too! DIY stores serve more of a function than simply forcing the price down. Most people get their information from these stores and they trust them to set the agenda that's right for their lifestyle.

‘ An estimated 400,000 US children 5 years old or younger have levels of lead in their bodies high enough to cause concern. ’

Center for Disease Control and Prevention, Atlanta, Georgia

# paints and volatile organic compounds

Paints have come a long way since the first eco-friendly efforts. You can imagine the painter's face when I suggested using a powder that you had to mix yourself to decorate the first Green Baby shop! But solvent-packed paint, according to the University of California, can contribute to Sick Building Syndrome, Danish Painters Syndrome (the occupational inhalation of organic solvents that can induce a kind of dementia, so called after a series of Danish articles linked it to exposure among painters), asthma, allergies and chemical sensitivities. I wanted to limit the amount of damage I was going to do to my staff and customers as well as the environment. In the end, cost drove me to plump for a low VOC (volatile organic compound) emulsion that is solvent free.

For asthmatics, breathing in a heady mix of chemicals can be really dangerous as an attack can constrict the airways and leave them fighting for breath. A whole swathe of evidence has been delivered by the environmental campaigners from Greenpeace and Friends of the Earth and WWF to prove that paints, varnishes, solvents, even flame retardants that have to be sprayed on so many domestic products, can all induce respiratory problems, particularly in young children. Just think how small your child's bedroom is and how close he sleeps to the walls. A Norwegian study on vinyl emissions concluded that an infant or child who sleeps in a smaller room is exposed to greater emissions.

Although you may have new environmental alternative paints to put on your walls you still need to sort out what is already there. Even the most cautious parents may not know the risk to their children from lead paint hazards in their own homes. Health experts estimate that one in ten British children still suffer from lead poisoning.

Experts are warning that its very presence in old paint poses a higher risk to the nation's health than previously thought. Old leaded paints have the potential to poison young children and pose an occupational hazard to decorators, joiners, plumbers and electricians who ingest or inhale contaminated lead dust resulting from decorating, building work or paint stripping operations in old houses, even years after work is complete.

Until the 1960s, lead-containing pigments such as white lead were widely used in oil-based domestic and industrial paints. Lead is toxic to many of the body's tissues and enzymes, and small children are most at risk to lead poisoning as it accumulates in their nervous system while their bodies develop. Death by lead poisoning is uncommon, but dangerous levels are thought to be one of the reasons for lower intelligence and poor school performance. It was only banned in 1978 by the Consumer Products Safety Commission, so it may well be lurking in the walls of your house. Clay plaster can absorb these types of toxins, but serves best as a primer to an organic paint as it forms a fine dust when it dries.

Although paints are now lead free there are still environmental and health issues to be considered. VOC-free paints have fewer chemicals than low-VOC paints but they are more expensive. They're worth it though; they can reduce your carbon footprint by up to 30 kg (66 lb). More and more eco-friendly brands are appearing on the market now that the manufacturers have cottoned on to the fact that there's money to be made out of the new self-interested, eco-aware consumer.

Some paints are now made using natural raw ingredients such as plant oils and resins, plant dyes and essential oils; natural minerals such as clay, chalk and talcum; milk casein, natural latex, beeswax, earth and mineral dyes. Water-based natural paints give off almost no smell and oil-based natural paints usually have a pleasant fragrance of citrus or essential oils. Allergies and sensitivities to these paints are rare and even if

## REACH

Greenpeace's REACH (Registration, Evaluation and Authorization of Chemicals) campaign for a toxin-free future was finally approved on 18 December 2006, by implementing EU law to limit hazardous chemical importation and production. REACH will cover 30,000 of the 100,000 chemicals available on the market and comes into force in June 2007.

your baby is not particularly sensitive, these paints are probably the safest for your health and certainly for the environment.

Old alternatives such as hemp, which was banned during Prohibition in the United States, when it was thought that too many Americans were smoking the stuff, may soon come back on to the market place. Hemp farming records go back 5,000 years (to China) but the hemp industry probably started in ancient Egypt. Hemp oil has a natural drying agent and was used in paints, varnishes and sealants that made rendered wood highly resistant to water. In fact, up until 1937 when synthetics exploded on the American market, all quality paints were made with a base of hemp oil. The cost of the oil will prevent any mass marketing of it until the American political climate allows widespread cultivation of hemp again.

# *flooring from sustainable resources*

You probably haven't given much thought to the nursery other than whether it should be pink or blue. But if you are thinking about the environmental impact of your choices for your nursery, then the rule is pretty straightforward – the fewer chemicals you use, the greener your nursery and the healthier your baby.

If you suspect that your child may have, or already has, respiratory problems, you might consider the Greenpeace study in Norway, which found that children living in homes that had PVC floors had a higher incidence of bronchial obstruction than children living in homes with wooden floors. Plasticizers in the PVC were thought to be the main problem. They concluded that it was because children tend to be more at risk because they are closer to the source of the problem when they crawl around on the floor.

Actually, flooring is a nightmare. If you want to be truly green you can use birch ply, the offcuts of the wood rather than the planks, but you'll have to then use the glue that contains formaldehyde, which is carcinogenic. Carpeting options are a minefield; I plumped for an expensive wool carpet because it was the only natural option on the market at the time.

Old carpets have already off-gassed chemicals so there is really no need to replace them. The best bet is a wooden floor, preferably with underfloor heating. In fact, new Building Regulations that came into effect in April 2007 will encourage more people to use underfloor heating because it is seen as one of the most successful ways of achieving the new demand for 15 per cent reduction in energy use for naturally ventilated buildings (20 per cent for air conditioned). The regulations also stipulate that, if possible, 10 per cent of energy use should come from renewable energy sources; underfloor heating runs at lower flow temperatures than radiator systems, which means that fuel can be used more efficiently. Crucially, it is also possible to make more effective use of renewable energy sources if you invest in under floorheating.

What kind of wooden floor you put over it is a question of whose ethics you find least questionable. UK DIY giant B&Q is committed to saving endangered forests and 85 per cent of its most popular teak, pine, balau and roble woods are sourced through the FSC (Forest Stewardship Council) and Tropical Forest Trust schemes. Ikea's environmental policy is pretty reputable and progressive for a family-run shop from which 1 per cent of the global population buys its furniture, but it is still cutting down far too many trees in Russia to make its flooring and other furniture. Ikea joined forces with Greenpeace in 1999 to phase out the use of wood products from endangered ancient forests and uses fast-growing beech as its favoured wood source, which is more sustainable than most trees that take years to grow again. Fast-growing acacia trees in Poland are thought to be the next big market in furniture.

It is expected of all big companies to have an environmental or social responsibility policy, and Ikea does buy some FSC wood but not all. Its labelling policy makes it almost impossible to tell which wood is from sustainable sources. But the World Wildlife Fund and Friends of the Earth have congratulated Ikea on its phasing out of hazardous chemicals.

The best option, particularly now that I realize how many stains end up on expensive wool carpets, is a wooden floor covered with a rug. It's easy to keep clean and if you look out for the RugMark label, which is a recent certification supported by children's charities such as UNICEF, you can do your bit to ensure that the carpet industry is working to end illegal child labour and to offer educational opportunities to children in South Asia.

If all this sounds like one of those scaremongering campaigns to create a market for new flooring, maybe it's no bad thing. There are more and more flooring alternatives than ever before, most of which are more energy efficient, reducing your carbon footprint and lowering the heating bills. Cork flooring has made a comeback, with tiles made from the outer bark of the cork oak in Spain and Portugal extremely popular, and heavy cold flooring such as marble, slate or ceramic is used more and more in homes where glass is optimized for solar gain. One of the problems with some eco-homes is the mass of glass, which can make your house as hot as a greenhouse even in midwinter. With a cold floor the heat is absorbed, retained and levelled out, while in the summer, it keeps the house cool. Remember to ask your supplier where your flooring is sourced as you don't want to find your floor tiles have been shipped halfway around the world.

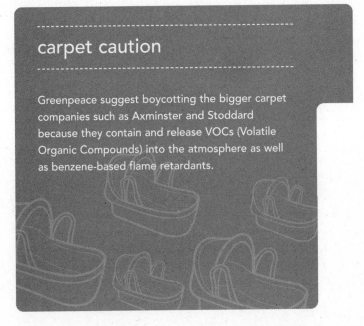

## carpet caution

Greenpeace suggest boycotting the bigger carpet companies such as Axminster and Stoddard because they contain and release VOCs (Volatile Organic Compounds) into the atmosphere as well as benzene-based flame retardants.

# beds and wooden furniture

Your baby is going to spend an awful lot of time in his bed so
what it is made of is very important. Initially, I found it very
difficult to find suppliers of furniture made of anything other
than MDF. Any solid wood nursery furniture I found ended up
costing a fortune as well as weighing a tonne. We had to find
a compromise for our customers. For those who can afford it,
a solid wood bed made of natural sustainable beech is an
ideal solution. For most of us, a happy middle ground will
suffice. My choice was affordable furniture with environmental
credentials, containing no formaldehyde in the glue, no
lacquer and definitely from sustainable wood sources.

If you've got a cot already, don't throw it away on account of
the formaldehyde that will almost certainly be in the glue. The
problem is not for the end user, but for the original
manufacturer who had to breathe the carcinogens and whose
skin was absorbing it while he was making the cot. Again, it's
important the consumer doesn't get paranoid. The planet really
doesn't need new parents throwing their old cots away and
buying another one because of some misinformed belief that
their baby will suffer. Apparently, spider plants help to absorb
the formaldehyde anyway. I don't know if they have them in the
cot factories, but it wouldn't harm to put one in the nursery,
would it? Being green is about thinking twice before you buy
rather than feeling guilty about the things that you already
have. It's the future that we can change, not the past.

We're playing with the idea of making furniture out of rubber
wood now. Although planting rubber plantations destroys the
local rainforests, the trees themselves only have a ten-year life

span before being burnt down. We're looking for ways of making use out of them so that they provide some extra income for the local people and make some good come out of a disastrous planting policy.

When we first began selling natural furniture, the product range was very limited. I had been reading up on the lacquer on furniture and how bedding had to be sprayed with chemical fire retardants that have been linked with skin allergies and respiratory problems, and it was all quite scary. The strict fire regulations were originally designed to stop people smoking in bed, but kids don't smoke! Even pyjamas or nighties have to be sprayed! What's worse is that it is not compulsory to include this information on the label.

## natural rubber or latex

Natural rubber is harvested by tapping the milk (sap) of *Hevea brasiliensis*, the common rubber tree, which grows within 10 degrees of the Equator. The rubber-tree sap is whipped up and turned into a latex foam. This is truly a sustainable resource because sap can be collected from the trees up to 180 days per year and the tree heals within one hour.

Apparently pyjamas might catch alight in front of open fires. In the meantime these kids spend years inhaling these chemicals just so that there's not the remotest possibility of them catching fire. It's a strange old argument, isn't it?

## *mattresses and SIDS*

Although the argument for buying organic cotton bedding is pretty straightforward, there is a lot of anxiety around cot mattresses. It must be the most common concern raised in my shops. An enormous amount of people remember a link between PVC mattresses and cot death, although they may not have even seen 1994's *The Cook Report* on ITV.

The programme created panic among parents when it claimed that 400 had died in one year from a toxic gas called stibine, formed when babies' urine is mixed with antimony, a metallic element used in the fire retardants for some plastic cot-mattress covers. The presenter, Roger Cook, said that the action of micro-organisms on fire-retardant chemicals can 'produce poisonous gases similar in action to nerve gases'. It was alarming stuff, made even more memorable when TV personality Anne Diamond's baby son died suddenly at four months old and she joined the campaign. The response was phenomenal; stores removed mattresses from sale and 50,000 people called an emergency phone line and were told to wrap suspect mattresses in polythene. It was later disclosed that at least three cot-death babies died on these wrapped mattresses.

Four years and £500,000 ($984,750) of public money later, the Institute of Cot Death concluded that there was no evidence to support it. Its chair, the Countess of Limerick said, 'Parents can be reassured that the toxic gas hypothesis and the claims put forward on *The Cook Report* do not stand up to scientific scrutiny.' It wasn't the only report to dismiss the claims; Sir Kenneth Calman, the Chief Medical Officer at the time, said: 'We had already looked at the hypothesis in the Turner report, which came to the same conclusions.'

# the case for natural mattresses

There is still a lot we have to do to persuade parents why they should buy a natural mattress. A recent survey found that more parents are worried about mattresses than they are about smoking during pregnancy. It's the same old story; if it doesn't come from the earth, don't touch it! Polyurethane foam mattresses constantly break down and release chemicals that are known carcinogens. Add to that the fact that they could be sprayed with fire retardants and your baby is sleeping on a bed of chemicals. It may not be an immediate killer, but if you can avoid it, why wouldn't you?

Alternatives began to appear after *The Cook Report* including baby futons with cotton covers. In fact that's one of the reasons the futon became popular. People always seem more interested in natural alternatives after a scare, particularly when it's to do with children. Our ancestors slept on mattresses filled with leaves and grass, held together with animal skins, but there are a few more sophisticated ones on the market these days. The one that I like and continue to sell has a stuffing of natural coconut fibre (a modern-day equivalent of traditional horse hair) called coir. Latex mattresses are becoming popular because of their ability to resist dust mites, the main cause of allergies, and fully organic mattresses are now available although they do work out quite expensive for most parents. The mattresses have unbleached organic cotton covers and a filling of organic coir, wool or natural latex or a combination, and pass the British safety standards without using any chemical fire retardants because of the use of lanolin from the wool. Wool fillers are very popular because wool is a natural temperature regulator; it keeps you warm when it is cold and cool when it is warm. Natural fibres are breathable and allow the sweat to evaporate and cool your baby down. Surely if your baby is not overheating at night, he's going to sleep better?

Although natural mattresses are a bit more expensive, they can be handed down through the family because of the quality. Hand-me-down mattresses have been used through families for centuries, but again, there is a scare around them. Sudden Infant Death Syndrome (SIDS) still claims the life of a baby every day in the UK and no one has yet discovered why, but the Foundation for the Study of Infant Death (FSID) is concentrating its research into links between bacteria growing in mattresses and their effect on some vulnerable babies.

Experts from the Scottish Cot Death Trust wrote in the *British Medical Journal*: 'There is a valid statistical association between sudden infant death syndrome and use of an infant mattress previously used by another child, particularly from another home' but it concluded that 'there remains insufficient evidence to establish a cause and effect relation'. Dr Richard Wilson, a paediatrician speaking on behalf of FSID, said: 'Babies are safest sleeping on their backs on clean, firm, well-fitting mattresses. Mattresses with complete PVC, or removable

## the case for organic cotton

United States farmers applied nearly one-third of a pound of chemical fertilizers and pesticides for every pound of cotton harvested (these chemicals are the most toxic classified by the Environmental Protection Agency). This can account for 25 per cent of all the pesticides used in the United States. The use of chemicals in producing cotton can lead to massive environmental and health problems.

washable covers are easiest to keep clean and there is no need for each baby to have a new mattress.'

For parents who don't want to take the risk, old mattresses are being trialed as part of a bed recycling scheme by FEAT Enterprises in Scotland, which deconstructs mattresses and other bed parts and sorts them into their component parts such as cotton, foam, fabric, coconut hair and springs. They are then baled and sold or passed on to other companies to create new products such as hanging baskets or trellises.

# *moses baskets*

Some may feel that a Moses basket may be a bit of a waste, both environmentally and economically, but it does make sense to have one in those first few weeks, even if your baby is sleeping in your bed with you. Sometimes it's handy when you need a bit of space to yourself. A Moses basket is so portable that your baby can be put down to sleep anywhere. For me the cot bed that I had bought for him just seemed too big but as soon as your baby gets too long or too heavy – usually only around 10 kg (22 lb), your Moses basket becomes redundant. I ended up passing mine on to one of my friends, but I have been told that they make very good toy baskets when you have finished with them.

We used to sell cots and cribs as well as cot beds at Green Baby but I soon realized how pointless that was. Cots and cribs are only useful for a short space of time. A cot bed seems a much more practical choice because height adjustments makes it easy to convert to a bed when your child is ready for it. I had to convert ours to a bed when Thomas was still pretty young. He had an amazing skill for climbing out of the cot bed, so the safest option for me was to put him into the bed instead.

# wallpapers

Wallpapers are not paper at all but vinyl and may contain hormone-disrupting phthalates. The glues used to stick the wallpaper on may also contain chemicals, so you may want to think twice about what you use on your baby's nursery walls. Over time the chemicals will evaporate into the atmosphere, a process called off-gassing. Formaldehyde products are found in everything from kitchen cabinets, carpeting, pressed wood products, particleboard, plywood, medium-density fibre (MDF) board and panelling used in furniture manufacturing to shopping bags, waxed papers, facial tissues and paper towels.

Emissions are thought to be most harmful during the first 365 days. The best bet is to try and decorate a few months before your baby is born, and keep the room ventilated. Although there are now low-VOC wallpaper glues available and wallpaper made of cotton and wood, these can be expensive for most parents. The most economic and environmental alternative to decorating the walls may be to use stencils using natural paints.

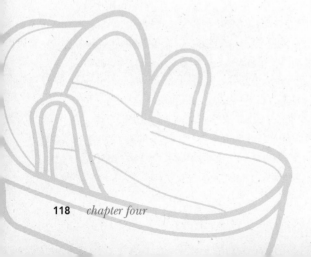

# curtains and blinds

If you are concerned about allergies and asthma, it might be an idea to avoid curtains unless you have the time to wash them frequently. If you do go for curtains, use natural rather than synthetic fabrics. If you are choosing blinds, try and avoid the vinyl ones as they may contain PVC. Metal ones made of aluminium or steel work well and can come in nice colours to match your nursery. One of the most environmental choices is wooden or bamboo blinds. These can be lacquered, so do let them off-gas for a few days before putting them in the nursery. Blinds tend to be vinyl so try and find ones made of natural materials. The roller ones can gather dust so you may need to vacuum them every couple of weeks.

# baby baths

As a new mother you are given masses of 'useful' advice from parents who have been there before you. Most of it you can take or leave, but one I grabbed was the myth of the baby bath. I found it better to use a bath support that you can use to support your newborn in a normal bathtub. Made of towelling-type fabric, it looks like a type of reclining seat with a wire frame. Your baby's head is supported above the water, which is great if he doesn't like water, and it allows you to wash your baby while he is supported and he is less able to wriggle and slip as he would in a plastic baby bath. It's also particularly useful if you're trying to reduce all that paraphernalia while travelling. Although I chose not to buy a baby bath to save some money, I can sit back now and think

> **Buy organic cotton toys for young babies as they go straight into their mouths.**

how happy I am that I didn't leave a bathtub-size carbon print on the environment!

## *toys*

The mantra we have to practise is 'reduce, reuse, recycle', especially as parents usually spend about £10,000 ($19,695) in the first year. What we all have to show for it, and more importantly, what our children have to show for it, is an indictment of the consumer society that has contributed to the mess we're in now. So instead of packing your baby's shelves with things that he will probably never play with, think about what stimulates babies at different ages. Energy-saving lights that project moving images on the shade will serve a dual purpose of casting delightful shadows on the walls and ceiling while lighting the room. Babies love music, so instead of relying on Classic FM's latest range of hot-housing favourites, make your own up or mumble through the ones you learnt at that baby music group. And you don't need to spend a fortune on dolls if socks make great puppets! Your baby will be entranced by your creativity!

As they grow, babies will make their own toys any way. Watch any child in any country in the world, including ours, and they are amazingly creative with a twig or a bit of sand or the box that their toy came in! Montessori education suggests that if you want your child's imagination and sense of self-sufficiency to grow, look no further than the natural world he lives in.

Some toys serve a real purpose, although I still maintain that a baby will find a way to support himself while he's learning to walk without relying on a wooden walker. Baby walkers with bricks are fun though and will entertain him for hours without him taking the house apart to find something equivalent to build. Rattles and teething toys are also very useful to chew on instead of stuffing anything and everything else in his mouth.

Of course people will always buy toys but they are not an essential item and it's often hard to justify the cost. People are always going to need nappies, but nobody thinks about how important it is for a baby's toy to be made out of organic cotton. What does a baby do as soon as you give him a toy? It goes straight into his mouth. Can you imagine the conditions under which those £1 ($1.96) polyester toys you see everywhere were made in China? If you buy your toys from China, you have to accept that you are probably buying children's toys made by children. How comfortable do you feel about that?

It's so much more expensive making a toy out of organic cotton, but we justify the cost by getting them made by a really excellent Fairtrade project in Egypt. A company called Under the Nile makes the toys and they are manufactured by a community project called Sekem. The cotton they use is biodynamic, which is one stage further than organic, using pheromones to control cotton insects. This system was developed by scientists and farmers for the first time in Egypt and was so successful when Sekem used it with cereals, herbs and vegetables that the project has subsequently grown into a rich community of businesses, schools and non-profit societies that employs about 2,000 people.

So many toys on the market get through the net because people think that wooden toys are green. But there is wood and there is wood. I remember a guy came to me trying to sell UK-made rattles. I had been thinking about how we really should support locally produced goods so I was interested in what he had to offer. The rattles turned out to be made of Canadian maple wood, shipped from Canada to Taiwan to be produced and assembled in the UK. I was horrified. I said 'No, way; I can't even contemplate doing that.' Much as I loved those rattles, I wasn't prepared to buy them for the shop.

## the continuum concept

This is the Jean Liedloff philosophy that believes that keeping your baby close at all times, sleeping with him and trusting him to follow your lead, nurtures a happier, more self-disciplined, co-operative baby.

# *sheepskins*

Sheepskins are a multi-purpose must-have. I bought one for Thomas when he was born and it was one of the best things I ever bought. We still use it as a bedside mat eight years later. Sheepskins are incredibly useful in keeping your baby's environment feeling and smelling the same at all times. If you put one in a buggy, a travel cot or down on the carpet at a friend's house, he will feel secure and very probably go straight to sleep. I remember my uncle saying that everyone in the dog world knows that if you rub a sheepskin on the mother when you give the puppies away, they settle more easily in a strange environment because the dog can still smell the mother. Of course, it all makes sense.

I know that sheepskins work a treat but like many natural products there is some debate about them. There are some researchers who believe that babies should never sleep on sheepskins, with one study in New Zealand even linking it to cot death. Research was not conclusive and didn't take into account other factors such as the fact that many of those who use sheepskins in Maori culture are big smokers. I leave it to you to draw your own conclusions.

A lot of the products come from different cultures that seem to have parenting sussed. Slings, which allow you to get on with the housework, while your baby snuggles into you, have changed people's lives. Dads are able to bond with their babies and still get on with their day. But to get hold of some of the really good ones like Huggababy, you used to have to go round to someone's house because they were sold by a group of individuals rather than from a shop or by mail order in the very early days. Many of them were also preaching the Continuum Concept. You would get this whole life-changing information and, if you wanted to, access to a network of like-minded parents while you were buying your sling.

# key principles

Remember always that where your baby is concerned the more natural his environment, particularly anywhere that he spends much of his time, such as the nursery, the healthier he will be.

- Avoid using PVC floors in the nursery. PVC brings a high risk of your baby inhaling phthalates because he is so close to the floor

- Choose wooden floors rather than carpets or vinyl flooring

- Use environmentally friendly, VOC-free or low-VOC paints, which are the safest for your health and for the environment

- Check paint tins and household and DIY products such as varnishes, paint strippers, wood preservatives, aerosol sprays, disinfectants and air fresheners for VOCs (volatile organic compounds)

- Use only what you really need. Reuse existing materials; recycle your own wood and source any new materials from sustainable resources

- Wash cotton covers at 60°C (140°F), the required temperature to kill dust mites and bacteria

- Buy from sustainable sources and ask your suppliers if they support any social projects

# chapter five

# WHAT A WASTE

# disposables, washables and their effect on the environment

For such little people, babies create a lot of waste. Disposable nappies with their cocktail of super-absorbent chemicals, paper pulps and unbiodegradable plastics account for half a family's weekly rubbish – that's nearly half a tonne each year! British babies will get through three billion nappies this year – and next, and the next, unless we start changing our habits.

Even if every parent in the country were to change to washables right now, every disposable nappy produced in the last 15 years would still continue to slowly ferment deep under the ground in our landfills. Researchers predict that some parts of disposable nappies would take 500 years to degrade. At least they're no longer piled high for the local wildlife to help themselves to; this generation of babies' leftovers, including live viruses such as the polio vaccine, are leaching into the ground and leaving the rest for the seagulls to snack on while councils try to find room to bury them. No wonder The World Health Organization has called for an end to 'the inclusion of urine and faecal matter in landfill sites'.

If we dispose of around 2 million tonnes of carbon every day, simply in the amount of hot air we expel into the atmosphere, imagine how much methane is being produced from nappies dumped on landfill sites. Local authorities in the UK are trying desperately to reduce biodegradable waste in landfill sites, and with so much methane being produced,

## disposable nappy facts

According to a recent life cycle analysis (LCA) commissioned by the Environment Agency in May 2005 to study the environmental impact of washables versus disposables, in two and a half years of nappy use, disposable nappies will:

- Create a waste pile of 99 kg (218 lb) of plastic and 76 kg (167 lb) of paper

- Have an environmental impact equivalent to driving a car over 1,300 miles

- Require 93 kg (205 lb) of crude oil to manufacture and transport

- Contribute 626 kg (1,379 lb) of $CO_2$ to global warming

This is based on an assumption that the average parent uses 4.16 disposable nappies per day.

they see no environmental advantage to using 'biodegradable' nappies at all. It's poo that's the problem. The answer is simple; flush it down the toilet and wash that nappy before using it again.

When we first become parents, it's astonishing how quickly we morph from being barely at home, creating no rubbish at all, to becoming a family responsible for three bin bags every day. A daily mountain of tetra paks, baby wipes and nappy sacks is dumped outside the back door while we get on with working out the basics of getting through the day with a new baby.

For most of us, it's a good couple of months before we join the real nappy gang. We spend several weeks first dumping those plastic disposables in the rubbish bin without a second thought. By the time we have our epiphany – in my case, my baby's nappy rash from hell – and consider the washable options, we have barely given a thought to the impact we are having on our environment.

## nappy facts

In the late 1990s, WEN and the Real Nappy Association (RNA) compiled statistics from midwives and paediatricians and found that each baby uses 5,020 nappies in an average two and a half-year period, this means eight to twelve per day for newborns; six per day for older babies. They concluded that home-washed nappies could save up to £1,000 ($1,969) per baby.

6 Disposable nappies account for half a family's weekly rubbish – that's nearly half a tonne each year. 9

# the history of change

The work that organizations like the Women's Environmental Network (WEN) have put into getting washable nappies on to the public agenda has to be applauded. Now that the papers are full of climate-change stories, now that we're beginning to accept that we may well be running out of oil and that the 'long decline' that scientists have been talking about for decades is actually about to begin, we need to give credit to the people who were so determined to make nappies the big issue for new parents. This was the market that they reckoned would be up for changing their habits.

This was before a phrase like 'climate chaos' described the rising number of freak weather conditions, and it was the killer campaign that hit the spot for new parents: those chemicals in disposable nappies were not just ruining the planet for our next generation but they might even affect our children's sexuality. Environmentalists discovered that this was what the market was *really* interested in.

Canadians had already discovered the sinister properties of disposable nappies with a story about polar bears who were eating gel-filled nappies from the landfill sites and becoming hermaphrodite. I cannot confirm the accuracy of the story but Canadians took notice of it. I don't know if it was because people love polar bears or whether they were worried that the chemicals might have the same effect on their baby boys, but it seemed that Canada was suddenly leading the world in a nappy revolution.

## getting political

The indestructible, gender-bending power of disposable
nappies was enough to bring the issue to the attention of
Parliament. Gina Purmann, the woman behind the Real Nappy
campaign at WEN had an extreme stance. She commissioned
art students to take really disgusting photographs for an
exhibition at the House of Commons. There were
photos of dirty nappies piled in the middle of
a playground, and seagulls tucking into
excrement-filled nappies dumped into a
landfill site. The exhibition certainly
attracted those MPs' attention and they
really got the message! Some of these
early campaigners get forgotten; they tend
to be the unsung heroes whose passion and
commitment put so many backs up, but whose
bloody-mindedness is what got the issue noticed.
Gina Purmann, I salute you!

# laundry services and the reality of using washables

Encouraging parents to get their hands dirty washing nappies
was perceived to be the biggest problem in changing the
mindset of new mothers. We are so used to outsourcing our
least favourite domestic responsibilities that nappy laundry
services seemed to be the most likely answer. Nappy services
were springing up in cities across the Western world in the
late Nineties. Soiled nappies are collected from customers in

special nappy bins, clean washables are provided, followed by the delivery of freshly laundered nappies a week later.

Campaigners believe that the environmental footprint of the laundry service is better than home laundering because industrial machines are so much more energy efficient than domestic washing machines. Nappy services also use biodegradable detergents rather than harmful phosphates, which means no toxic chemicals leaching into the water supply. Compare this with the waste water from the manufacture of the pulp, paper and plastics used in disposable nappies that contains dioxins, solvents, sludge and heavy metals. WEN figured that one van picking up a number of nappies is also better than umpteen cars driving off to the shop to buy the washables.

However, that presumes that everyone in one area is using the same method, and we know that it's not like that in reality. Many of these nappy laundry services actually turn down custom because clients are too scattered, and the increased use of petrol is too much of an ethical and economical consideration. It might work in urban areas, in the bigger cities, but not in rural areas. WEN got letters from people all over the country asking for more information. Every

‘ Some parts of disposable nappies will take 500 years to biodegrade. ’

single letter asked 'Where can I buy these washables?' Not one of them asked, 'Who's going to do my laundry?'

Besides, laundry services are not cheap. Although popular with some, for the majority of parents, changing to washables is about saving money *and* the environment. With a laundry service, you may be saving the environment but you're not saving money. If washables are only available to the middle classes, a huge chunk of the market will never get green.

## *council initiatives*

Councils have to be creative if they are to meet targets and avoid paying fines. They can promote recycling in general, but they can also offer parents using real nappies financial rewards. Recycling doesn't save them money, but encouraging the use of washables can. Several councils trialled recycling boxes on doorsteps and took the opportunity to distribute leaflets with them promoting washables and informing people about the environmental impact of disposable nappies. Some councils even use cash-back incentives or free nappies in an attempt to encourage parents to think twice about dumping disposable nappies.

## council targets

It is estimated that disposable nappies account for 2–3 per cent of all household waste in the UK – that's 400,000 tonnes of waste each year. This works out at an estimated cost to councils of between £100,000–£200,000 ($196,950–$393,900) per annum in landfill. It is therefore in the councils' interests to promote re-usable nappies. European Union legislation in 2000 declared that councils would be fined if they were not meeting new landfill regulations, which aimed at a 65 per cent reduction in municipal waste going to landfill by 2020. Councils were given targets and funds to help meet the targets.

Campaigners started going out on the streets, trying to tempt locals to come and talk to them about washable nappies. They explained how washables could save money *and* the environment. Nappy boards appeared at markets, giving people an opportunity to touch and feel this new type of nappy and see how much had changed since the days when their parents were soaking dirty nappies in buckets of bleach. People could discuss their nappy-using habits with real parents rather than listen to the PR messages from the disposable nappy giants on the television.

# confusion campaign

After years of campaigning resulting in a real growth in the use of washables, it didn't help when the Environment Agency published its first findings of what would be a four-year Life Cycle Analysis (LCA) in 2001. It claimed that real nappies were just as bad for the environment as disposables because of the energy used in washing, drying and ironing them. Ann Link of WEN, who had been on the panel, but had not been shown the final conclusions prior to publication, argued that the Environment Agency hadn't accounted for the energy used in manufacturing the nappies. She pointed out that if parents were to wash 24 nappies rather than the 47 that the LCA assumes, using an 'A' energy-rated washing machine at 60°C (140°F), they will have approximately 24 per cent less impact on global warming than the report says.

By 2005, the Environment Agency had spent £200,000 ($411,000) on the study and WEN accused them of missing the point, 'This lifecycle analysis is a wasted opportunity to put the long-standing debate about nappies and the environment to rest,' said Ann Link. 'It says what most other LCAs have: that both systems use similar amounts of energy but the disposable  system uses more materials and puts more into landfill. Even in its current flawed state it shows parents who use cloth nappies can save waste confident in the knowledge that washing them will cause no more global warming than disposable nappies.'

The research was largely discredited and WEN lodged a complaint against the Absorbent Hygiene Products Manufacturers Association (AHPMA) with the Advertising

Standards Authority for flouting a 1992 ruling by claiming in a leaflet aimed at new parents that there is nothing to choose between the environmental impact of disposable and washable nappies.

AHPMA members such as Proctor & Gamble were forced to remove their claims from disposable nappy adverts in the UK. In the US 90 per cent of American babies wear disposable 'diapers', which takes 82,000 tons of plastic and 1.3 million tons of wood pulp – that's 250,000 trees – to manufacture. To the nappy campaigners and lobbyists, it was the culmination of a long slog to put washable nappies on the mainstream agenda and a great day for the washable world.

# save money by switching to washables

For many there's an economic motivator; every time we use a disposable nappy, that's around 20p (39 cents) spent. With a washable nappy, that's around 20p (39 cents) saved. For others, it's the sudden realization after yet another nappy change that if it's three bin bags a day for your baby, how many must you, your friends and their friends be dumping in landfill sites? And by the time you're slapping on the nappy cream, you've got a vision of all those babies born every year and the millions of nappies that are being chucked into landfill sites each year.

Real nappies may not be mainstream yet (according to Mintel, the market research company, 10 per cent of parents use washable nappies). Somehow, despite the financial benefits, washable nappies have become a middle-class trend, appealing to those who want to save the environment rather than those who want to save money. Every year in the UK, the Real Nappy Association in association with WEN, launches Real Nappy Week, with celebrity endorsement and grant funding to promote washables. Although it brings a great

## washable nappy economics

The economics of washable nappies need to be really spelled out:

- A whole set of washables for one baby's entire nappy-wearing life costs around £150

- The washing costs another £400 based on a two-and-a-half-year lifespan

Compare that with the average spend on disposables:

- Disposables for one baby's nappy-wearing life cost £1,250

- Factor in another one or two babies per family and you're spending a hell of a lot of unnecessary cash

- The price goes up again if you're using certain premium brand nappies; those prices are based on own-brand nappies

amount of attention to the washable nappy campaign through various stunts such as photography exhibitions, nappy fashion shows, 'nappuccino' mornings, nappy mountain building and other events, it still doesn't make a real impact on the majority of the population who believe that if a nappy is not wet, it doesn't have to be changed. Because the chemicals in disposables absorb so effectively, many parents think that they can leave them on for most of the day.

The real issue with washable nappies seems to be about reusing them, about passing them down to other children. This is something that the British seem to find so alien. But I've heard stories of parents using the same washables for five kids. Think how much money they saved! And there are more savings to be made by getting your baby out of nappies earlier as well. Many of my customers believe that potty training is much easier when babies wear washables because they don't like to be wet.

## *washables are cool!*

Our obsession with celebrity has changed the face of green parenting. It's no longer a bunch of hemp-wearing hippies, but a cool new breed of jumble-sale chic models, actors and singers who are championing waste reduction. They are not just buying washables, but feeding their babies organic food and putting them on the back of their bikes to avoid the car. It's a great message to get to the world that devours that kind of information.

# *the chemical explosion*

One of the biggest tabloid stories fed by the celebrity pack was the link between chemicals and health problems. The rise in interest was shown most acutely in natural toiletries, but for those whose babies had eczema, washables were seen as the obvious answer. There does seem to be an argument for using breathable cotton washable nappies if your baby's skin is particularly sensitive to chemicals. For my own baby, switching to organic 100 per cent cotton immediately got rid of the nappy rash that had plagued us both since he was tiny.

## *hormone disruptors*

The toxic load in disposable nappies is a story that I try to keep in perspective. It's too easy to create a scare about inconclusive

------------------------------------------------------

### startling research

------------------------------------------------------

Did you know that a little boy's testicles will be as much as 1°C (1.8°F) hotter in disposables than cloth, according to the October 2000 issue of the American *Archives of Disease in Childhood*. The report suggests a link with the significant rise in male infertility over the last 25 years.

reports that suggest that the chemicals in a baby's disposable plastic-lined nappy can trigger any number of worrying conditions. But there are plenty of stories I can tell you, of course. Dioxin, which in various forms has been shown to cause cancer, birth defects, liver damage and skin diseases, is a by-product of the paper-bleaching process used in manufacturing disposable nappies. Those little crystals you spot on your baby's genitals after changing him are super-absorbent polymers (SAPs), which absorbs up to 100 times their weight in water. Absorbent polymers were used in tampons in the 1980s but were removed after a possible link to toxic shock syndrome. Nothing has been proved about the long-term effects on a baby, but I suggest you input these chemicals on Google and see if you're still happy to put them next to your baby's skin.

Greenpeace's conclusions were pretty clear about the use of chemicals in disposables, and they were not impressed with the nappy giants' response to their report in May 2000. Greenpeace's scientific test results contradicted a statement by Procter & Gamble, in which the company denied that its nappies were contaminated with organotin compounds. Greenpeace's toxics expert, Thilo Maack, said: 'The reaction of Procter & Gamble is a scandal. The company is downplaying the danger instead of actively searching for the source of the long-lasting toxic endocrine disruptor, TBT (tributyltin) in Pampers. It is absolutely irresponsible to expose babies to these extremely toxic substances. The fact is that TBT is one of the most toxic substances ever made, and it is being spread through the skin and contaminates the environment as well as people.'

In July 2000, WEN released results of chemical analysis of five types of newborn-size nappies that showed the presence of tributyltin. Although the amounts are tiny, babies could be in contact with up to 3.6 times the estimated tolerable daily intake, absorbing it through the skin. A safe level has not been established for effects on the hormone system but the World Health Organization has calculated a tolerable daily intake for adults of 15 millionths of a gram. WEN estimates that intake of 1 microgram (1ug) a day could be unsafe for babies.

A report by Dr Rosalind C. Anderson, of Anderson Laboratories in West Hartford, Vermont, also in 2000, linked the childhood asthma epidemic to the chemicals in disposables. She didn't believe that asthma could be explained solely on the basis of what she termed, 'the usual suspects: dust mites, cockroaches, maternal smoking. Maybe child-care products (such as) plastic diapers ... plastic baby bottles, and plastic toys are important factors (through the release of) chemicals with toxic effects.'

The mice used in Dr Anderson's study developed broncho-constriction, the narrowing of air passages in the lungs as a response to certain odours and substances. 'It's similar to when asthmatics smell perfume and all of a sudden their chests get tight,' explained Dr Anderson, who suggested that until such time as this asthma-inducing effect can be confirmed in humans, avoidance is 'the only proper action'.

My feeling about this is the same as my feelings about organic clothing, food and toiletries; if it doesn't come from the earth or isn't good for the planet, just give it a miss. There are plenty of really easy options now and we're running out of excuses to give them a go.

# green disposables

We all have busy lives and using washables may not always be practical, especially when travelling. For some parents, it is just impossible to use washable nappies, but they would like to use a more environmentally friendly nappy. When I had my baby, there was no environmentally friendly option to disposable nappies in the UK. When I discovered just how sensitive Thomas was to the gel in disposables, I decided that he could never use them again. I did some research and found that there was a disposable nappy in the United States that was gel-free. Instead of the super-absorbing gel, it used cotton blended with chlorine-free wood pulp. The owner of the company had, like me, been inspired to find something for his own daughter and when he found a tiny company in Colorado making just what he was looking for, he was so impressed that he bought the company!

I persuaded him to let me be the exclusive distributor in Europe of Tushies nappies as well as their natural wipes. It seemed to make perfect sense to offer both options to parents. This nappy is not fully biodegradable but it works just as well as other disposables and it does not use the chemical super-absorbent.

Since then we have seen other brands of disposables come onto the market making various environmental claims; chlorine-free, unbleached, made from cornflour and other renewable resources. It is great that steps are being made to improve the environmental impact of disposables, but none of them address the huge problem of the waste issue.

Let's be clear though; there is no such thing as a biodegradable disposable nappy. All disposables contain plastic. Even if they use more expensive cornflour technology to create a biodegradable nappy in the UK, we just do not have the conditions for that nappy to degrade. Capped landfill sites do not allow air to circulate to break down the components. Every single one of the new generation of environmental nappies on the supermarket shelves contain super-absorber gel except Tushies.

I am sure improvements will continue to be made to the more environmentally friendly nappies while the big companies concentrate on rolling out new improved versions every year that allow your baby to jump, run and crawl while wearing them. Greener nappies are taking shelf space away from the giants and, as always, consumer power will make the giants change their ways. With the climate-change story shifting gear, large companies will have to listen and use some of their huge profits to research sustainable alternatives to conventional nappies. In the meantime, washable nappies are the only genuinely green choice for the environment.

## changing nappies

It's often the practicalities that stop many parents from making the leap towards using washables. But parents can't be complacent any more about putting what they know about the environmental impact of nappies into action; there is even talk among the serious scientists about the need for rationing. But in the meantime, it always helps to know that it's far easier than you think!

Washables are no longer bulky towelling stuck together with giant safety pins. They are made out of all sorts of materials, from the standard absorbent cotton to fantastic new sustainable materials like hemp and bamboo and 100 per cent organic cotton. Today, there are around 50 different types of reusables, mostly fitted, and without a safety pin in sight. Even the fastenings are easy – Velcro, Aplix or poppers, and once snapped into position, the nappies are worn under smart outer wraps or pants, often decorated with elephants or dolphins, and made out of the latest waterproof fabrics on the market. We have become spoilt for choice and for places to buy nappies. You can pick them up in your local baby shop, online, at the supermarket, at the nearest pharmacy or at your favourite department store.

Changing a washable nappy is as easy as putting it on. The 100 per cent biodegradable, flushable liners catch the faeces and can be flushed straight down the loo. Wet and soiled nappies are tossed into a nappy bucket until there's enough of a load to wash. Modern-day washing machines do a fantastic job of getting nappies clean without boiling them as our parents or grandparents used to do. As long as a stain isn't allowed to dry, it should come out. If stains are stubborn, one of the many natural-based stain removers on the market or nappy soak powders are designed for just this purpose.

Knowing when to change a washable nappy is a lot easier to figure out than a disposable. Unlike the chemical-packed disposable nappies, you can feel when a nappy is wet. Just put your hand inside the outer pant and touch the wet cotton. Most of the cotton nappies soak up the urine naturally, but the weight of them will give you the biggest clue as to when to change. Remember, don't panic if you can't change the nappy as soon as it is wet; the cotton will absorb most of it until you can get to a suitable place to change your baby.

# *nappy systems*

The use of the nappy plus the wrap or pant is called a nappy system and can be made up from any brand of nappies and outer pants/wraps according to what suits you and your baby. The wrap fastens at the front or the sides, while a pant tends to be a pull-up style to go over the nappy, and when fixed firmly, will not leak. Nappies are not a fine science but once you've found the formula and you've got a routine, you'll know how tight to fasten them. At first you think you're going to cut the circulation off, but after a while you crack the method; you realize that tight is the key to no leaking. When you change a baby 5,000 times over the course of his two-and-a-half years of incontinence, you'll get to know just how tight a nappy needs to be and you will find the system that works best for you!

Babies are different shapes and some nappies suit some babies better than others. Some parents prefer the good old-fashioned terries that they probably wore when they were infants. Babies can also get particular about certain sounds and get on better with popper fastenings rather than the Velcro or Aplix. This is a consumer society and even when you're selling environmentally friendly nappies, it is choice that people want. The popular baby magazines are always reviewing new styles on the market and often the best-selling nappy on the market depends on the kind of review it receives.  Everyone's baby is different so trusting one reviewer's recommendation doesn't seem the best way to choose. I always think you need to try out a few different types before you decide to invest in a full set.

# *fabrics*

The fabric of a nappy is crucial to your lifestyle. Living in the middle of the city without the luxury of drying space, you will need a quick-drying nappy such as flannelette. Your newly environmental stand to line-dry, even in your postage stamp of a back garden, will make terries a bit more of a chore to dry, but consider the impact on the environment of a dryer before you turn it on. Terry towelling, despite being the market leader as the most absorbent, will take longer to dry, but if you have a garden, put it on the washing line – as long as it's not raining. If your baby suffers from allergies to pollen, be aware that in the height of summer, all your washing will be soaking up the pollen, so you should not hang it outside.

Many large companies are now selling 'real nappies' as they call washables, on the high street and online these days. But there are still not enough large retail outlets stocking them as standard. According to buyers, they are seen as a 'potential growth market', and as we head into the 'long decline' predicted by climate scientists, it can't be long before retailers begin to tap into the climate-change industry and market washable nappies to their customers as 'added value'.

## key principles

Many of us might think that washables are too much like hard work because they are more time consuming and awkward to use. The simple truth is that the level of sophistication and ease of use in washable nappies these days, plus the fact that they work out so much cheaper, ought to change your nappy-buying habits if you are not already a committed eco-campaigner!

- Buy washable nappies because most disposables contain the carcinogen, dioxin, from the paper-bleaching process during manufacture and account for half a family's weekly rubbish – that's nearly half a tonne each year

- If your disposable nappy goes to a landfill site, live viruses such as the polio vaccine will leach into the ground

- You will use 5,020 nappies in an average two-and-a-half-year period. That is 8–12 per day for newborns and 6 per day for older babies

- Ring a nappy service and get your washables collected and laundered. Nappy services use biodegradable detergents and their machines are energy efficient

- If you use reusable washable nappies, you will use three-and-a-half times less energy, 90 times less renewable materials and 8 times less non-reusable materials than if you use disposables

- Don't let stains on your washables dry or they won't come out

- If stains are stubborn, use a natural-based stain remover

- If you live in an urban area where it's difficult to dry outside, buy flannelette nappies that are fast-drying

- If your baby suffers from allergies to pollen, don't hang your washing outside

- Find out if your local council has cash-back incentives or offers free nappies if you use washables

# chapter six

# GREENING THE BATHROOM

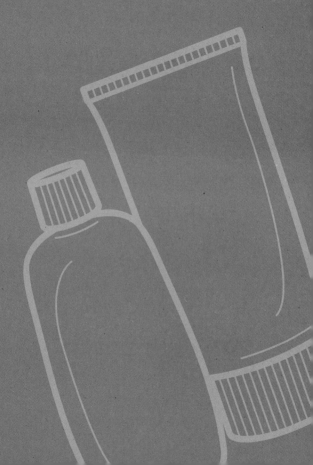

# *your child's skin*

It's no surprise to me that of all the natural products that we sell, it's the organic toiletries that are the top sellers. A lot of people come to us because their babies have asthma and eczema, rashes and other skin problems, and they are looking for solutions. I always use my experience with Thomas' skin problems to advise them what to do about it. Over the years of talking to many, many parents, one conclusion we have all come to is that the perfumes and chemicals in the products we were using seemed to be the problem. We watched what seemed like miraculous results on our babies' various skin issues when we tried calendula and chamomile instead, and we have been hooked ever since.

The skin is the body's largest organ and if you slap a cream full of chemicals on it, around 60 per cent will travel directly into the bloodstream. If it's a concoction of things you've never heard of, you might think twice before smearing it on your baby's bottom. His skin is generally around five times thinner than an adult's. Remember the rule of thumb: if you can't eat it, don't put it on your skin.

# what the campaigners say about our toiletries

Campaigners like the Women's Environmental Network (WEN) and Greenpeace, which will publish its REACH report later this year, have proved that our straw poll was right. The synthetic fragrances in baby wipes and petrochemicals in that concoction we used to use when we first became parents have all been 'outed' as the enemies in your cupboards. It's the whole drive to make things cheaper that has encouraged all these companies to use so much junk, and it is the 'Roddick factor' (after Anita Roddick, the founder of The Body Shop), the passion of people who make and support natural products and the movement that has grown up around them, that has woken us up to what we have been putting on our skin and hair. We took for granted that ingredients were safe in the products we had grown up with. In the meantime, the big companies were substituting natural ingredients with synthetic ones in a bid to bring costs down.

Up until recently many products did not have to disclose their full ingredient list, something that is still true for nappies. In the US it took 'the Terminator', Arnold Schwarzenegger, now Governor of California, to call the industry to account, and sign a first-in-the-nation bill requiring cosmetics companies to disclose ingredients linked to cancer, birth defects or reproductive harm. The 'Safe Cosmetics Act' came into effect in 2005. Once again, the advice is simple: if the ingredients list is full of big long names that you've never heard of, it's got to be scary. The only time I'll try and pronounce something is when I can tell it's the Latin name for an essential oil!

# chemicals to avoid

Parabens and phthalates were selected by WEN as the two worst ingredients, and the most commonly found in many products, and the foaming agent, sodium lauryl sulphate (SLS) has not just been associated with eczema and with skin and eye irritation, but also linked with cancer. Propylene glycol stearate can alter the actual structure of the skin, allowing other chemicals to get deeper into it, and increasing the amounts of other chemicals that reach the bloodstream. It has been linked with skin conditions such as eczema and dermatitis.

Parabens have become one of the most widely used preservatives. Scientists back in the 1930s developed synthetic methyl, ethyl and propyl parabens from benzoic acid as low cost, non-smelly preservatives that could be used to kill bacteria, fungus and yeasts in shampoos, bubble baths, nappy rash ointment, baby wipes, lotions and toothpaste. But since then, parabens have been found in cancerous tumours, and particularly in breast tissue. A report from Kyoto University found that parabens penetrate the skin and get into the bloodstream and Heildelburg, Reading and Brunel Universities have all concluded that they are oestrogen mimics and have been implicated in a number of health issues. The Soil Association – the UK's leading certifier of organic products – is reassuring the public that such chemicals are not permitted in healthcare products that carry its symbol. Aluminium and zirconium, which have also been found in human breast tumours, are similarly not allowed under the Soil Association's standards.

Phthalates, found in synthetic fragrances (also called parfum) have been linked to reproductive damage. You'll find them in your nail polish, hair spray and in the fragrances that are added to some baby wipes. Researchers from Lund University in Sweden found that prolonged exposure to hair dyes, sprays and other products was the probable cause of babies being born with problems such as heart defects.

Phthalates are a hormone disruptor and classified by the US Environmental Protection Agency as a 'probable human carcinogen'. The fact that they are largely linked to ovarian and breast cancer should be enough to remove them from most family's shopping lists. The European Union is so concerned by the risk of them leaking out of plastics when chewed that is has banned the use of phthalates in teething toys for children under the age of three.

But WEN discovered that both of these oestrogen mimics are particularly dangerous to babies, small children and teenagers who are at various important stages of hormonal development. They admit that no one is quite sure of the full extent of the adverse effect they may have during these vulnerable periods, but why put it to the test when there are so many answers in the natural world? Go on, have a look now at the gender benders you've already got in your bathroom!

Finding alternatives on the high street is tricky. Even Lush, which sells itself on the freshness of its natural products, uses parabens as a preservative, as well as SLS to foam up its otherwise natural ingredients. Gina Rolf at Lush explained: 'We work on using ingredients which have a safe history of use, and parabens have a safer history than any other preservative. Preservatives are not the loveliest ingredients that could go in cosmetics but without them all liquid products deteriorate. Lush's answer is to make over two-thirds of our products solid so we use very little. We also make fresh unpreserved face masks which are kept in the fridge and have a shelf life of three weeks. For a company that produces a full range of cosmetics and toiletries, we must use proportionately less preservatives than any other company. When there is a safer more effective alternative available, Lush will switch to it. At the moment there is nothing safer available.'

The Body Shop might not use SLS in any of its products, but I was really surprised to find parabens in many of its hair and skin products, despite the fact that even the shop assistants were fully clued up about the concerns. Shelley Simmons of The Body Shop explained: 'Parabens are used as a preservative in a number of The Body Shop products. They are clearly identified on the ingredient lists. At present, there are no plans to phase these materials out, but we will continue to monitor scientific evidence and customer concerns. It should be noted that, as a matter of policy, The Body Shop products are being formulated specifically to minimize the use of preservatives.'

Abi Weeds of Essential Care says that some of the bigger companies use parabens because they're cheap and allow for the 'long, bullet-proof shelf life that only the parabens offer. The truly natural preservative systems can only achieve a shelf life of 12 months (some semi-synthetic preservatives like phenoxyethanol and alcohol can achieve two years),' she says. 'But that's too short for many companies that might have large volumes of stock sitting around.' It is much cheaper to produce a huge batch of product that can be stored for ages, than to keep producing small batches to keep the stock fresh. 'This is what we and a lot of the companies producing real organic products have to do' she explained, 'even though it's much less profitable. It's also what we'd prefer to do. No matter what anyone says, good vegetable oils and precious herbal extracts lose their potency and nutritional and therapeutic properties as they age, even if they don't go mouldy or off.'

Essential Care are always researching new preservative systems that vary from product to product. 'We do our best to manage with essential oils, herbs, lichens and enzymes,' says Abi. 'A lot of the German natural beauty companies use alcohol to preserve, but this isn't always ideal for the skin and it presents cultural issues for some people. You only strictly need preservatives in water-based products (only balms based on oils won't go off), but you need water to make products with light texture such as lotions and functional products like shampoo, and also to work with a lot of water-soluble herbs like aloe vera.'

The Body Shop claims to have discovered 'a truly innovative formula development' to avoid using any preservatives in its aloe range, and we can only encourage them to try to find something for the rest of its range. We know that there are alternatives; natural preservatives and antibacterial ingredients such as honey, sugar and alcohol, and plant extracts such as rose, cinnamon, cloves, calendula and vanilla have been used

❝ It might discourage you from buying a skin product with propylene glycol stearate in it, if you know that it is an ingredient in antifreeze! ❞

as preservatives for centuries and are allowable under Soil Association standards. The SA also allows natural processes such as heat treatment, removing oxygen through vacuum packing, and ensuring a low water content to prevent the fast spread of bacteria.

# natural products and babies

While there is any doubt at all, surely the only way to go is to use organic products, although most of the time babies need nothing more than a bit of soap and water. Instead of chemical-based creams, nature offers more than enough herbs to heal most of our ailments. If you buy from your local health food shops, or the increasing number of specialists (like Neal's Yard, Whole Foods, Organic Pharmacy and Planet Organic) who often employ naturopaths, nutritionists and herbalists to talk you through the reasons for colic, teething pain and all those other baby complaints, shopping will never be the same again. You'll learn so much about the way that your body works that emptying the supermarket medicinal shelves will never have the same appeal. You don't need to live in the big cities to shop with these companies either as most will do mail order if you give them a call or you can visit their websites (see Resources).

Besides, pharmaceutical companies make millions out of copying natural products and creating synthetic versions, so cut out the middle man and stock up on what nature grows instead. Despite the parallel growth of skin allergies and cancers, our trust in the great gods of consumerism has overpowered our trust in our own garden. It's undoubtedly part of the story of how we lost touch with the planet.

Herbs have been around for as long as there has been soil rich enough to grow them, and history is littered with tales of wise women and witch doctors who have channelled their healing properties – and been burnt at the stake for their trouble. The story of the past 30 years in natural toiletries is also about exceptional people. But the emphasis has been more on the pioneers who went out into the world to find exotic plants and flowers and earthy tribes: Anita Roddick who brought body rituals of women from all over the world into The Body Shop and made cosmetics political; Alfred Vogel who brought us Echinacea from a Sioux Indian in South Dakota called Ben Black Elk and introduced us to our own immune systems; and Romy Fraser who put organic on the national agenda when she founded Neal's Yard, the first shop in the UK to sell certified organic essential oils.

For me, it was a man called Neil who did a disappearing trick with Thomas's nappy rash! He made a lovely milk bath out of milk powder and chamomile, which cleared up one of Thomas' rashes immediately. After that, he was the one who inspired all our original toiletries. I would look at some of the revolting baby products on the market and ask him to make me up something using natural ingredients. I remember smearing on the concoction that came in my free hospital sample pack and thinking how gross it was, so Neil discovered how to make petroleum-free jelly out of beeswax.

My doctor had suggested that I use olive oil for Thomas's cradle cap, but I always thought it made him smell like a salad! I asked Neil about an alternative and he went off to consult his books and came up with a potion of sunflower, safflower and jojoba, a pretty easy combination to make at

# a guide to essential oils

Vital Touch (see Resources) suggest that you stick to a few essential oils that have been used extensively with good results:

- Lavender (*Lavandula angustifolia*), Chamomile (Roman), Ravensara (which is antiviral and a decongestant like Eucaplytus but much gentler and appropriate for babies and kids), Mandarin, Tea Tree, Lemon

- Always buy from a reputable supplier – you need to use 100 per cent pure essential oils, sold with an integral dropper in the body

- Never use essential oils undiluted on the skin

- Always follow directions

- Never take any essential oils internally

- Always keep essential oils out of reach of children, and away from eyes and pets

- Essential oils are very powerful – if in doubt contact a qualified aromatherapist (the Kevala Centre has a list of reputable international practioners).

- Use lavender or chamomile hydrolats for babies under six months. They contain some of the same properties of the plant material of essential oils

- For babies of six months and older, dilute one drop of the essential oil in an egg-cupful of milk first. Whisk it well so that all of the oil is evenly mixed in the milk. This is very important to ensure that no neat oil comes in contact with the eyes or the mucous membranes. Neat oil will float on the surface of the water and it can get into the baby's hands. If he then rubs his eyes, you will be in trouble.

home and it is still a real success story with our customers. I think the secret is leaving the oil on for at least 12 hours or overnight before using a fine comb to comb it out of the hair. We can't make any medicinal claims for it without paying lots of money to do the clinical trials. Consequently we call it scalp oil and say in the accompanying information that it can help to remove cradle cap. We keep all the testimonials, but it continues to sell well and that's trial enough for us.

There are lots of good reasons for using some of the natural lotions and potions on the market; organic oils and creams are food for your baby's skin and can be extremely soothing. You just need to feel comfortable with the ingredient listing and understand what you are buying. If a product is labelled hypoallergenic it does not necessarily mean it is nonallergenic to everyone. It just means that it doesn't contain ingredients that are common allergens. Many essential oils (including commonly used lavender) are considered an allergen so ask an expert before you buy. You can test the product out on yourself first and then on a small area of your baby to ensure that he is not allergic.

# baby massage

If touch is the first language of babies, there's nothing like massage to get your message across. Baby massage bonds parents to babies and babies to parents like nothing else, but it is also a lifesaver. It doesn't just help them off to sleep but also deals with their digestive problems including colic, particularly in the early weeks and months. In the United States in the early 1900s, 80 per cent of institutionalized babies and children were dying, despite being well fed and kept clean. Gradually experts realized that they were dying from lack of touch!

A lot of parents feel worried about holding and touching their brand-new babies; they seem so tiny and fragile. Many of us have never even held a newborn before we have our own. Massaging him or her can be calming for both parent and baby and a great time to gain confidence with each other. But just as importantly, it stimulates the immune system and promotes the growth of myelin, the protective insulation around motor nerves that enables nerve impulses to travel faster. That means that their fine motor skills may develop more quickly. Add some mood enhancing aromatherapy oils and you've got a magic combination.

Reflexology in babies and children is another wonderfully bonding experience for baby and parent, and helps to keep your baby super-healthy. Massaging the crunchy crystalline deposits from waste products that accumulate around nerve endings on the foot can disperse them, as well as stimulating the lymphatic system's natural waste disposal service. My customers tell me that their babies often get almost immediate relief, and even hyper older kids fall asleep! It's a fantastic feeling when you realize what you can do yourself to calm or heal your own child.

# common bathroom items and their natural alternatives

There are a number of items that are found in every bathroom and we probably wouldn't normally question their inclusion. But, as you will have learned throughout this book, despite the fact that these items are in everyday use, it does not follow that they are good for you. The same old rule of thumb applies, read the label and if there is something you don't like the sound of, then buy a healthier alternative.

## baby wipes

Parents are brainwashed into buying so many of those 'nappy bag essentials' like baby wipes, but I was left wondering where to put the dirty ones. They really have to be one of the worst inventions ever – perfumed and non-biodegradable? How is that going to help your baby or the planet? Your midwife will probably tell you that you don't need to use the

*Avoid fragrances and fragranced products – babies are far more sensitive than adults.*

## baby wipe data

Remember the following points about commercial baby wipes and the natural alternatives.

- Most commercial baby wipes contain alcohol and perfume, which can dry your baby's skin and could aggravate or may trigger an episode of eczema or dermatitis

- Baby wipes are often impregnated with chemicals as well as contributing to the waste problem

- Use a flannel and water instead of a baby wipe – it can be washed and reused instead of thrown away

- For newborns, cotton wool and water is all that is needed. The best wipe for both your baby and the environment is a washable wipe, preferably made from organic unbleached cotton. Buy a dozen or so washable wipes and use them with a home-made wipe solution or water.

disposable wipes on a newborn anyway. Cotton wool and water do the trick for the first few months. Mine also told me not to get obsessed with baths; a baby's skin has to develop naturally and dries out if you bathe him too often.

It was when I went back to Canada that I discovered both Tushies disposable wipes as well as some fantastic washable wipe options. Tushies wipes were pretty much the first ones I found that didn't have any junk in them. The ingredient list was made up of words I actually recognized, and they were free of alcohol, which I knew already to be very drying. The Tushies wipes were also free of fragrance (that gender-bending chemical listed as parfum). Again, it's just common sense to avoid using perfume on a baby's skin, and you only have to sniff one of them to think about what might be in it. There are lots of theories about rising cases of asthma and eczema or dermatitis and one thing is for sure, alcohol and smelly perfume can't be helping the condition.

The washable wipe, a mini version of adult washcloths, designed with babies in mind, has a multitude of uses and is the most environmental and economical option. Unlike the one-use-wonder wipes, these are wipes for life; once your baby has finished with them, they can be used for dusters, floor cleaners and then on the pets. Invest in a dozen or so washable wipes and then you can even make your own formula to go with them.

# baby powder

There are also some natural products that confuse parents. Take talc. Talc is a mineral that occurs naturally and because of its ability to absorb moisture, people have been using it for years on both babies and themselves. Although there have been no conclusive studies linking talc to cancer, there is enough evidence for most cosmetic companies to remove it from their baby powders. It is not banned so it can still be used, but you will find most baby powders call themselves talc-free and use a natural alternative such as cornflour.

There is some evidence to suggest that babies have died by inhaling the fine talc-powder dust, but it is the talc miners who have been the most affected. Talc is closely related to the potent carcinogen asbestos, and it is the people working with the industrial grade talc that seem to show higher rates of lung cancer and other respiratory illnesses. Being a green parent is not always just about keeping your baby safe; it's about accepting your responsibility as a consumer to ensure that what you use is safe all the way down the supply chain.

But baby powder really is an essential. My chubby baby had so many rolls of baby fat it was impossible to dry every nook and cranny. By using a powder after the bath, any moisture I missed was absorbed. As summers get hotter across the Western world, it is also a fantastic product for humid climates; my friends living in Bali say it is a must for any tropical baby. There are plenty of natural talc-free alternatives now on the market that work just as well. Neil found out that Native Americans used arrowroot, which was apparently for soothing arrow wounds, so we added it to our talc-free powder and the customers loved it.

# nappy rash

Most babies will get nappy rash at some time in their lives. It may be a symptom of teething or a reaction to new foods, detergents, perfumes or other chemicals used in some disposable nappies, wipes or lotions. However, nappy rash is usually the result of sitting too long in a soiled nappy, so it's best to take the nappy off and leave it off. You might even pay more attention to your baby's toilet rhythms and fast-track the potty-training process with it off! And before you say it's impossible to train a tiny baby, how else do you think those African mothers who carry their babies on their back know how to time their babies' ablutions? Die-hard greenies see it as the answer to the nappy-waste debate.

Treating a sore bottom could be as simple as letting air to it. Just because your mother did, you don't have to reach for the Vaseline. In fact, you're more likely to reach for something that your grandmother or great grandmother used such as calendula cream. Using a nappy cream daily after changes creates a barrier between the nappy and your baby's skin, but remember that 60 per cent of it will head directly into the bloodstream so choose a natural product if any.

# Petroleum-based products

Another questionable ingredient that has been passed down for generations is petrolatum, the main ingredient for petroleum jelly. Petrolatum is refined before it is used in beauty products but this by-product of the petroleum industry has been listed as a probable human carcinogen in the European Union's Dangerous Substances Directive.

A review by scientists from Lawrence Berkeley National Laboratory showed that as many as one of every five chemical carcinogens causes mammary tumours in laboratory studies, indicating that the breast is more sensitive to carcinogens than almost any other tissue in the body.

The cosmetic, toiletry and perfumery industries, whose members are the manufacturers and brand owners of cosmetic and personal care products and ingredient suppliers, are keen to point out that under the EU Cosmetics Directive and its implementation in the UK, products placed on the market must be safe and not cause harm to human health. It insists that this is why only highly purified petrolatum can be used in cosmetics, and claims that it is not carcinogenic.

The story is different in the USA where refined grades of petrolatum are used in personal care products. 'Products labelled "Skin Protectants" are sold over the counter,' says Joan Thomas of the CPTI (Cosmetic, Toiletry and Perfumery Industry). Petrolatum is one of the allowed active ingredients but it must be United States Pharmacopeia (USP) Grade, which she says is not carcinogenic. In the USA, there are companies that make non-USP grade petrolatum for personal care but this material is also highly refined and must meet California requirements. It's a tricky argument if you want to use the stuff.

## soaps and shampoos

Babies have wonderfully delicate skin and so it is best not to disturb it too much. Although cotton wool and water will suffice for the first months of dribble and drool there will come a stage when your baby is crawling about and getting dirty. You may decide to use soap so it is important to understand what is available. Soap is a fat – either animal or vegetable and for obvious reasons it is best to choose a vegetable-based soap for your baby. Do rinse it off properly though and avoid antibacterial soaps, which are too harsh for babies and absolutely unnecessary.

Kids love bubble baths but all those bubbles do not occur naturally. Sodium lauryl sulphate (SLS) is the bubble maker that you need to look out for on ingredient lists and has been linked to urinary tract irritation and infection. A few drops of natural baby shampoo or body wash in the bath will give enough bubbles and will limit the chances of any adverse effects.

# toothpaste

Toothpaste is a subject that has created great debate as to whether to use fluoride or not. Dentists say that it's necessary to avoid cavities, but it may well be the first chemical concoction that your child will swallow when they start brushing those first bottom teeth. You should always monitor a small child's brushing to ensure that he spits the paste and water in the sink rather than swallows it all; a child's liver and kidneys are especially susceptible to fluoride toxicity, although it would take an enormous amount to have any effect. As with all these things, common sense should prevail; just be sure he spits the stuff out.

You may also want to think about the toothbrush you use. With natural animal bristle brushes available (although they are not suitable for vegans) this is another area where you can limit your child's exposure to chemicals.

It's tricky when we're listing the kind of ingredients to avoid to put it all into perspective and to remember that we are exposed to chemicals on a regular basis in our lives and still manage to live to tell the tale. Plenty of people use ordinary bathroom products with their babies to no apparent ill effect. The impact on the environment is also negligible when you're comparing the carbon emissions you're producing in one trip to the supermarket. But use your common sense; natural products are undoubtedly better for you, your baby and the planet and it's easy and far more pleasurable to use them. As you find what works best for you, try to buy online more and reduce your carbon footprint by leaving the car at home. The Soil Association has a regularly updated list of certified retailers on their website and most good retailers have deliveries now.

# read the label

Often the labelling of toiletries is confusing. Companies have to list all ingredients and say which one is organic. Often some products will use the word organic in the name and not contain a single organic ingredient. If a product contains 100 per cent organic ingredients then it may carry a certification such as the Soil Association Standard. The best advice is to read the label and decide.

Consumers should always make sure that there is a recycling emblem on the bottle or pot itself or on the label. Many good retailers, online and off, accept packaging back for reuse where possible and if it's not reusable, it goes for recycling.

Cut down on the products that you and your family use – much of the concern is about the 'cocktail effect' of the chemicals in the different products that we use. Many women are using over 20 different products a day, bombarding themselves with hundreds of different chemicals – is that eyelash conditioner really essential?

## key principles

When buying anything for the bathroom you really need to look at the label. There are often some nasty chemicals lurking in the prettiest of packages! Here are a few things you should look out for:

• Avoid products that contain sodium lauryl sulphate (SLS) and sodium laureth sulphate (SLES), which create bubbles in shampoos, bath products, toothpastes and mouth rinses. SLS has been associated with eczema and cancer

• Avoid shampoos, bubble baths, nappy rash ointment and toothpaste that contain parabens, which are suspected hormone disruptors. Look out for the following compounds: methylparaben, propylparaben, ethylparaben and butylparaben

- Check your nail polish and hairspray for phthalates, which are suspected hormone disruptors

- Check the 'fragrances' of scented products , they may contain diethanolamine (DEA), monoethanolamine (MEA), triethanolamine (TEA) and are sometimes preceded by 'cocamide'. There is concern that they may form nitrosamines (carcinogens)

- Look out for methyldibromo glutaronitrile (MDBGN) in cosmetic products

- Avoid products containing imidazolidinyl urea and diazolidinyl urea

- Avoid using talcum powder, which can be dangerous if inhaled and has been linked to a small risk of ovarian cancer when used in the genital area

- Do not use petroleum jelly, which is listed as a probable human carcinogen on the EU's Dangerous Substances Directive

- Avoid PVC containers, there are some perfectly recyclable plastics such as HDPE, PP and PET

# chapter seven

# GREENING YOUR WARDROBE

# the story behind your baby's clothes

With a new baby, planning a new wardrobe has probably never offered such a life-changing opportunity. Our buying choices are fundamental to what happens to the planet in the next few decades, and as parents that must be top on our list of priorities as we make a nest for our babies. The peak oil crisis, the long decline in which we have to slow down, use less and recycle is all about a rethink in the way we shop.

Food and clothing, which come from the soil and are mostly manufactured in and transported from the developing world, are central to the argument. With a growing argument to link the residue of those pesticides in our clothing and the leaching of them into our skin, choosing your baby's clothing over the next ten years really could make an enormous difference to the health of your child, millions of farmers, pickers and manufacturers all over the world, as well as to the future of the planet.

If your baby is yet to arrive, you'll probably be fantasizing about what he will look like in those cute little romper suits you have seen in the high street. You will probably look for something that is soft, comfortable and easy to change, wash and store. You might be thinking about buying breathable material such as cotton, which is healthier for your baby's skin than synthetics.

Maybe you have read up about flame retardants, which are sprayed on to some children's nightwear and which campaigners feel should be banned because of their heavy toxicity. Or you might simply be thinking about the cost of it all and opt for the cheapest, imagining that the cost of parenthood is going to be so prohibitive that you can't indulge in anything else.

## let it breathe

The skin, as the body's largest organ, needs to be able to breathe. Wrapped up all day in synthetic materials, which may have been dyed using formaldehyde finishing, arsenic and heavy metals, it's no wonder that those chemicals end up in his bloodstream. Cotton and other natural fabrics, such as wool and silk, breathe with your baby and, if they are organic, you can be sure that they won't have been dyed or bleached using harmful chemicals.

## *eczema, asthma and fabrics*

People whose babies suffer from skin or lung conditions such as eczema and asthma, have found that synthetics aggravate the situation; even polyester labels can send some babies into a scratching frenzy! Super-soft organic cotton is a godsend when you're trying to find something to soothe and cool your baby, particularly if it has mitts attached so that he can't scratch. My baby found great relief from his skin conditions with organic cotton, which meant that we did too!

There is growing evidence to support the link between fabrics and the aggravation of weaknesses in the immune system, which can lead to eczema, as well as asthma. With asthma, the argument lies in the proximity of a weak-lunged baby to pesticide residue and a cocktail of chemicals used in dyeing and finishing and flame retardants. Going for the organic option won't cure either condition, but it can avoid their development in the first place, as long as you reduce your baby's exposure to other toxic substances in his food and environment and boost his immune system naturally.

Some children have nickel or other metal allergies, and have reactions to fastenings such as poppers and buttons. As it's such a political no-no, as I explained in Chapter 3, we have a nickel-free zone at Green Baby.

# *the cost of cotton*

Organic cotton baby clothing is more expensive than its synthetic equivalent, and as your baby will outgrow his sleep suit before he has time to wear it out, the cost argument can be tricky. Of course, a well-made organic cotton garment can be passed on to your next child and on through the whole family, while a cheaper option will probably fall apart after its first owner has discarded it. It's often for that reason that many parents will spend more on better quality, but not necessarily organic baby clothes. Let's hope that the campaign by the big retailers to increase their organic cotton range will spread throughout the high street so that those parents with bigger budgets will find greener products right under their noses.

## how does your cotton grow?

Few people think about where their material comes from, the conditions under which it was made and what it took to get to your baby shop. Even fewer really know what organic means when applied to clothing; when I was on a TV programme recently, the presenter asked how clothing could be organic. She said she thought that organic just referred to fruit and vegetables.

Behind every babygro and washable nappy, every Fairtrade T-shirt and summer hat, there is the story of the cotton farmer, the ginner, the pattern maker, the cutter, the stitcher, the finisher, the product controller and the local wildlife whose health may have been affected by pesticides, and a whole eco-system to think about. What about the packaging, the air and sea miles, the retailing decisions that force those air miles up with late orders? Is anyone in that chain actually benefiting from your baby's little T-shirt?

## ❛ Skin conditions can be aggravated by synthetic materials.❜

# buying organic

Choosing to buy organic clothing means that you're thinking about the future, about what you personally can do to reverse the decades of poor agricultural practice. These poor practices are largely in the developing world where pesticides and fertilizers, genetically modified (GM) crops and soil mismanagement have decimated the eco-system; and where pesticides cause serious health problems among farmers who often lack the appropriate protective equipment and may not be able to read the instructions. In many villages in India and Africa where most of the world's cotton comes from and where hospitals are not always available, a family member who suffers from cancer has an enormous impact, physically and economically as well as spiritually on the rest of the community.

In the cotton fields of India and Africa, Non-Governmental Organizations (NGOs) and agricultural campaigners are working hard to encourage many farmers to replace the chemical pesticides they have become accustomed to over the years and turn their soil organic to protect their own health, the consumer's health and the health of the planet.

In India's Maharashtra, I learnt how farmers are taught how to use a natural alternative pesticide mix of garlic, chilli and tobacco. The pesticide lobby is really strong in India and in many of the developing countries, and their message is really persuasive; but most farmers still put their income before their health and would automatically think about spraying when they see insects destroying their crop. They have to get out of that mindset if the project is to work. Gijs Spoor, whose company Zameen Organics is behind an enormous campaign to increase organic agricultural production across India, told me about the sleepless nights he had when one of his transition farmers sprayed in a knee-jerk response after months and months of cleaning the soil. It meant that the whole area was ruined from one thoughtless spray.

It is a huge risk when farmers convert their soil to organic; although it doesn't cost them anything in output, it will cost them in time and effort while they clean the soil first and make their own compost. It takes three years for soil to be clean enough of the residue of pesticides to get organic certification and their productivity will go down at first. As they won't know for sure what the results will be, they only convert some of their land in the first season. Their entire income is dependent on it.

The success stories make it all worthwhile. One of the farmers has been organic for five years now and is already earning 30 per cent more than his neighbours. He showed me his house and his healthy family and told me that he is now able to invest in organic soya, which will reap even more rewards to plough back into that house of his. I'm sure the other farmers look at what he's got and think that with a little extra effort, they too could have it all. He showed me the compost he had made, picking up the stuff in his hands, crumbling all that old ox excrement he was so proud of, and asked me to feel it. He showed me the worms, which hadn't been seen in the local soil for years. He said he remembered that when the land belonged to his grandfather, it used to be packed with earthworms. Making organic compost and bringing that life back into the soil is like an art, and experts have to get right across the country to train the farmers and encourage them to keep going.

More farmers will convert to organic cotton when they see farmers clearly benefiting and recognize that the market is expanding. While there are people like Gijs and the organic farming associations of India at Zameen Organics coaching them about how to be organic and encouraging them to keep going through the transition period, the organic cotton market will continue to grow. When I was there, the women were looking for more projects such as toy making, and they are relying on people like me to come up with some plans. When I visit the villages I bring my Green Baby catalogue to show them and they are fascinated by the end product. It is something you as the consumer may take for granted, but these farmers have no idea where their hard work is going.

# *Fairtrade and the responsibility of the consumer*

When you're thinking about dressing up your little girl, you might consider how those hormone-disrupting chemicals in pesticides might be affecting the young girls working in cotton seed farms. Some communities in India believe that cotton seed can only be picked by virgins under the age of 16 who emasculate the hybrids to give a better yield. All hybrids are pesticide-treated at the time of their production, so how do you know if a cotton dress might have started life in the hands of a 12-year-old girl in some pesticide-drenched field in Maharashtra? The answer is simple; buy organic, or transition cotton at the very least, which is what Marks & Spencer's is supporting, and you've got your guarantee.

Some things are much trickier to resolve. Ginning, the process of spinning the raw cotton wool into yarn, like most agri-processing is seasonal work and relies on migrant labour rather than employing local people for only a few months of the year. Migrants move from farm to farm for the work and, of course, they take the whole family along. The children can't go to school because schools don't accept them for only four to five months of the year, and so they work on the fields to bring much needed cash into the family. What else are they going to do?

## mechanization

Increasing mechanization is a double-edged sword. One combine is equivalent to 100 or 200 people's livelihoods, and as ginning is becoming more mechanized it cuts out 40 per cent of the labour. This means that migrant labour isn't needed, but it also means that those people are going to the city where there is no work, and where they might end up living in a tent, and if they are lucky, selling vegetables for 40 rupees a day.

# social projects

Luckily there are people working in the cities to sort out this problem. My woven clothing is made in a factory in Hyderabad under a World Bank funded scheme to bring women and their daughters out of the slums. A lot of these families living below the poverty line depend on rain to earn a living; if the rains don't come, they simply don't get any money. Theirs is a real hand to mouth livelihood and very often they just don't have money to feed their children even a meal a day. The World Bank has got a new definition for this sector of society, the POP, the Poorest of the Poor, those who are so vulnerable and needy that even charities working with them say that they are challenging.

Meera Shenoy is a World Bank consultant who is the Executive Director of the Employment Generation and Marketing Mission (EGMM), a society created by the rural development department of the government of Andhra Pradesh, a southern state in India. EGMM addresses the needs of the next generation, the 18–24-year-olds. In the past, the social programmes in which the government has invested have not led to jobs, and that causes frustration and social problems in the cities where they have relocated to, or in the villages where they were expecting so much more. Now the training is to be linked to jobs in textiles, hospitality and other white-collar jobs, an organized labour market to which they won't have had access before. That means these young people get a monthly income for the family, even if they are working in the city and sending it back to the villages.

The city is overwhelming when they first arrive and Meera has built into her budget ways of helping them. She has founded a counselling service to help with the bureaucratic formalities that so often keep the illiterate out of the system. That helps to stem a lot of the fallout when things would otherwise just be too tough to cope with, and when somehow what they're used to, even abject poverty, can seem an easier option.

In 2006, EGMM linked 15,000 youths to jobs. In 2007, it will be 150,000. The country's employers realize now that there is a new labour pool opening up, and the government gets a higher return on its investment. For the poorest rural communities, it's a sustained way out of poverty. It sounds simple, but looking around our factory, I can see how it's working. The staff comprises women and their daughters from these communities, as well as skilled workers. Imagine if all the clothing manufacturers around the world were able to tie up with one of these social projects. Now, that's what I call Fairtrade.

# the Fairtrade Mark

In 2005, the Fairtrade Labelling Organization (FLO) established a set of criteria for Fairtrade cotton and this has since become the big buzz word, thanks to heavy marketing by the retail giants. The Fairtrade Mark is a certification system that means that any product which sports the label has been produced and distributed under an internationally agreed set of standards. These include minimum wages, toilets for the workers and suitable tea breaks and working hours. In more and more cases, social projects are being developed like those at the factories in India where our clothing production supports the growth of employment of deaf and dumb girls and exceptionally poor women and their daughters, and at Under the Nile in Egypt, the factory where our toys are made, which supports a community school. But it doesn't necessarily mean that your T-shirt is organic.

# consumer power: how to read a label

Labelling can be extremely confusing to the customer, and where there is confusion, scepticism generally follows. For example, Green Baby, the label and the shop is not certified Fairtrade or Organic but all our suppliers are. Although we have applied for Fairtrade certification, this takes time, and until then, we can prove that our suppliers use ethical and sustainable practices, but we will have to wait for the all-important certification. But where do you find that information on a label? Once people really understand what organic means, there will be less need for such labelling conundrums.

There is now increasing interest from the FLO in getting joint certification of Fairtrade and Organic. Currently a label can say 'Fairtrade' rather than 'Organic' as Marks & Spencer's cotton range does. But how can you be Fairtrade without being organic? How can you claim to protect workers' human rights when you may be endorsing their use of pesticides? We know that pesticides are harmful. Is it acceptable to buy a T-shirt that has been produced by someone who gets enough tea breaks in his working day but spends the rest of his day breathing in carcinogens? If some companies are not allowed to use the label because the social conditions at some of their manufacturing outlets don't meet Fairtrade standards, how can the others use the Fairtrade logo if pesticides have been used on their cotton?

What about the dyes and the bleaches? When we started our company, there wasn't an obvious way of whitening cotton without bleaching it. No one had investigated any alternatives; they just used bleach. It is incredibly difficult to pass all the tests to be certified organic and it costs a lot of money. The Soil Association sets tough standards for its certification and it's not always straightforward. You have to use viscose thread in garments for example, because it is a natural wood fibre, but to make yarn out of the wood, someone has to dye it. That's a heavy environmental issue, as well as a health issue for the person who has to dye it.

It's the same with plastics; if you use plastic buttons, you are using numerous chemicals that could affect the workers, so you have to find alternatives. Right now, our production manager is making buttons out of fibreglass and shells from Bali where she is involved in a toy-making project. That's what people are doing in this market, constantly trying to find new ideas that work, that don't harm anyone, and that can positively contribute to employment opportunities in the developing world. It takes time when you're in new territory, but to me it's got to be fair all the way along the supply chain. It's up to you as a parent to support these practices.

## air miles

Air miles are always an issue but unfortunately cotton doesn't grow in Britain so there will always be some sort of transport involved. We can and should support beautiful home-grown tweeds and felts, as well as organic leather and sheepskin in a bid to use up every little bit of that home-grown meat. See Chapter 4 for why babies love a sheepskin.

## packaging

Packaging and its impact on the environment is particularly tricky for retailers and I am constantly trying to find a solution; our clothing is imported from India so it has to be protected in plastic covers. Customs officers rifle through the boxes and the clothes would suffer if we didn't protect them. Anything that comes from Egypt, India and a number of other countries has to be frozen to keep the bugs at bay. And that means wrapping it in plastic.

We decided to use resealable bags made from recyclable plastic, but it's far from ideal as some councils are still not recycling plastic. Lobbying any council that doesn't is one answer, but designers need to find new ways to package more naturally. Carbon offsetting companies are funding new technologies, (see Chapter 8) and smart technology is already likely to shift air miles to ship miles, which could cut packaging waste by 50–60 per cent.

# the farmer's story: what we, the consumers, need to know

If being a green consumer means looking out for the entire supply chain, being part of the richer Western world means looking out for the needs of the entire global population. According to Pesticide Action Network (PAN), in the US, 25,000 cotton farmers are given $3.5 billion in subsidies as part of the US Farm Bill passed by President Bush in 2001. Two million farmers in West Africa get no subsidies at all, but have to deal with the consequences of lower world market prices as a result. We're talking about two million farming households that are producing cotton in West Africa, which, if each household is around 10–15 people, means that 30 million of the poorest people in the world are relying on cotton.

Most parts of Africa do not have the infrastructure to support Western-style garment manufacturing, and more than any other part of the world, the workers are badly exploited. We currently manufacture some of our Green Baby bedding in Europe using organic cotton sourced from Africa, but according to Camilla Toulmin, Director of the International Institute of Environment and Development (IIED) who spoke at the 2006 Rachel Carson Memorial Lecture, organized by Pesticide Action Network UK, organic cotton production in West Africa in particular has a dubious future.

Cotton production has doubled worldwide in the past 40 years, with India and China the main sources of growth, but African cotton production has increased ten times over the same period. West African farmers now account for around 5 per cent of total world production, but are the third or fourth largest exporters of cotton. If the Fairtrade conditions are not put in place, that's a hell of a lot of exploitation just to get those T-shirts into the shops.

Exploitation leads to health issues, which in turn leads to unemployment and whole communities being locked into poverty. Global poverty is one of the biggest headaches those kids of yours and mine are going to have to tackle by the time they're earning their living. PAN UK reported recently that Benin, Senegal, Burkina Faso, Mali and Cameroon are reintroducing the infamous organochloride insecticide (also known as organochlorines or chlorocarbons) into their cotton farms. USAID missions in West Africa are encouraging the development of 'new technologies', and training national scientists in various biotechnology skills to deal with the need for insecticides. However, with huge companies like Monsanto already introducing GM cotton, the fear is that once it is firmly established there, it will be next to impossible to establish an effective organic production system.

## responsible retail

The needs of the farmers and the needs of the environment are not always the top priority in the heady game of retail. When a big client puts an order in late, and then asks for it to be delivered early to beat the other stores with their spring collection, it means air-shipping the order instead of sea-shipping it. The cost to the environment can be enormous when a client changes his mind, but this happens all the time. It needs a policy change right at the top of these retail giants. It's not the consumer who wants a spring collection in January. That retail boss should educate the consumer as to why the company has taken this stance and describe what the impact is on the entire supply chain. This is what retail should call 'added value'.

We do need to give the companies that are going for ecological credibility a pat on the back rather than accusing them of jumping on the band wagon, but we should watch them carefully at the same time. I'm still buying more cotton than most of them, despite their big marketing campaigns, which suggest a different story. Some of the big chains who are making the most noise about Fairtrade are only dabbling with organic cotton baby clothing and putting them in just a couple of their stores nationwide. You have to assess what is lip service and what is an attempt to genuinely try out a new market.

# spinning a yarn?

Communication is vital in the retail business, but it has to translate into customer buying power rather than retail spin. Some large retailers have posters saying that they only sell Fairtrade coffee and tea, but you can't find it on the shelves. In one major retailer, they only sell it in their café. They're probably trying to figure out what the market wants without taking the risk, but they're confusing a lot of people because they think they should be selling what they say they're selling. Often you won't find Fairtrade clothes in the stores, it's only on mail order, but that's not what their marketing people say on the news when they launch their carbon-neutral plan. Make a noise; email their head offices, or, as PAN UK suggests, write to your MP to ask the government whether it intends using the enormous power associated with procuring goods and services to promote organic production. Campaign for trade and tax policies that encourage preferences for more sustainable products. At the moment, it's the other way round – producers of certified goods have to find funds to get certified and establish a separate supply chain. This is the time when consumer power can really make a difference.

## consumer power

Green Baby may still be one of the few shops on the high street to sell organic baby clothes, but things are changing. When we first opened, there was a very limited choice of organic clothing available on the market. In looking for pure cotton for my little boy, I spotted that cotton clothing didn't always turn out to be 100 per cent cotton, that there is no law against sneaking in 2 per cent polyester without saying so. Since 1999, the sale of organic baby clothing has grown and grown. You can now buy Green Baby products in department stores as well as in many baby shops around the country (see Resources). Larger stores, such as Tesco, Top Shop, Next and H&M, are all selling ranges of organic cotton now.

PAN UK urges us to encourage this market to expand, but also to call it to account. 'Tell the major retailers engaged with these initiatives that you approve of their strategy' it says in its Action Plan. 'Tell them not to niche market the ethical and organic goods, while driving a race to the bottom in the mainstream clothing market. Ask them how ethical it can be to sell organic and Fairtrade alongside £5 ($9.92) shirts and £3 ($5.95) jeans. It's impossible to pay a living wage or respect the environment when prices are so low. The recent report *Who pays for cheap clothes?* reveals a chain of misery and exploitation, polluted soils and poisoned water supplies. Retailers can drive a major improvement in prices and production systems, but they need to hear from you – the shopper – that this is what you want.'

There are lots of interesting companies out there wanting a piece of the environmental industry and that are looking at the eco-brands to see how to make them into seriously big business. There are also companies like Patagonia, Eddie Bauer, Mountain Equipment Co-op, Howies, People Tree, Green Fibres, Edun, Adili and others who are not just producing great organic clothing and contributing to Fairtrade, but who are actively encouraging their customers to think about how to change their throwaway mindset. The fact that Howies has just teamed up with Timberland is a landmark in retailing and the start of ethical partnerships catapulting the Fairtrade message into public consciousness.

# a vision of retail's future

The story of the past 30 years in textiles tells us so much about the crisis affecting the planet; the growth of the consumerist society, our seduction by a fashion industry that learnt to imitate, exploit and mass produce in the developing world, destroying its soil and harming its population. When the reserves finally ran dry, the retailers learnt to spin the information that campaigners had been telling them for the last 30 years to their advantage, adding value by enrolling their customers in a panic-driven bid to save the planet. Now Fairtrade is a marketing tool, with models and pop stars adding their names to the movement to buy ethically. It's easy to be cynical, but it's what turns us on and if it works, it's fine in my book.

The money and power of the big companies may bring the issues to public attention, and for that we salute them, but they need to get their organic range on the shop floor before we can really trust them. Support the big businesses as they dip their toes a little deeper into the Fairtrade and organic world, but also look out for the little shops who brought the market to their attention. Read the labels but also look out for the transition labels, and sharpen up your antennae for those who are abusing the system as well as those who are working hard to earn the cash to get certified.

# key principles

Choosing organic clothing for your child will not only benefit the health of you and your baby but also farmers, pickers and even the future of the planet

- Choose cotton and other natural fabrics such as wool; they breathe with your baby and if they are organic, they won't have been dyed or bleached using harmful chemicals

- Pass on a well-made organic garment to other children so the initial higher cost is offset by its durability

- If your clothes are cheap, ask yourself why. They may well have been made by children working in appalling conditions

- If your child has nickel or other metal allergies, watch out for reactions to fastenings such as poppers and buttons

- Avoid synthetic fabrics

- Support transition farmers. It takes three years for cotton to be clean of the residue of pesticides and to get organic certification

- Support Fairtrade products. The Fairtrade Mark certifies that any product that sports the label has been produced and distributed under an internationally agreed set of standards

- Write to your local MP to ask whether the government intends to promote organic production

- Campaign for trade and tax policies that provide positive preferences for more sustainable products. At the moment, it's the other way round – producers of certified goods have to find funds to get certified and establish a separate supply chain

# chapter eight

# TRAVELLING GREEN

# to travel or not?

For most of us, this is the real test of our commitment to
reducing our carbon footprint but it is a double-edged sword.
On the one hand, many of us would choose far-flung holiday
places with sun and sandy beaches given the option, but
long-haul flights are simply not good for the environment and
how many of us can afford travelling by sea in terms of time as
well as expense? On the other, we have to consider the effect
*not* travelling to exotic locations would have on their economy
when tourism is for many of these countries their principal
source of income. And if short-haul travel is the new littering,
are we really going to have to teach our children about the
world through TV and an atlas?

We all want to support global eco-tourism but know we
shouldn't travel long haul; we want to take our kids to the kind
of places that inspired our global social conscience, but at
what cost to the environment? Yes, to the train journeys
through Spain and Italy, but a ship to see granny in New
Zealand? Who's going to pay the mortgage while we're away
that long?

Richard Hammond, the eco-travel correspondent for *The
Guardian* and editor of greentraveller.co.uk says that there are
plenty of eco-holidays to choose from, like tagging turtles on
the Great Barrier Reef or community-based tours of Ethiopia,
but it's no way to salve your conscience. Although he says that
there are significant advantages that tourism can bring to a
destination, 'particularly in developing countries, through
creating jobs, stimulating local economies, and ensuring the
conservation of land and animals in protected areas,' there is

simply no way to justify 5 or 6 tonnes of carbon dioxide for the sake of a holiday. The only option, as far as he is concerned, is to travel by train. And environmental author, George Monbiot agrees, 'In almost all cases the atmospheric impact of the flight greatly outweighs any environmental savings during your holiday.'

But doesn't our global responsibility extend to the 10 per cent of jobs worldwide in the tourist business? 'Tourism is growing fastest in developing countries,' says Justin Francis of responsibletravel.com. 'For 50 per cent of developing countries, tourism is one of their top three exports.' All the solutions that have been suggested to tackle global warming require investment, but it's renewable energy, cleaner technologies, waste reduction processes, new science and rail transport, according to Justin, where the difference will really be seen. 'If we all stopped flying altogether the world would go into recession and we'd be less able to fund all of this,' he says.

# carbon offsetting

We've been travelling back and forth to Canada to visit my family since Thomas was three months old, something I need to reconcile with my green conscience. I have always been sceptical about the many carbon-offsetting companies that claim to be able to balance the carbon emissions of your flight by planting trees in sustainable rainforests. It just doesn't seem to get to the nub of the problem for me. It may absolve your conscience, but does it make you think twice about hopping on a flight again?

Business travellers are the least likely to curtail the number of their flights and the most likely to throw a bit of extra cash at the problem in the hope that it will go away. Carbon offsetting seems to me to be letting us all off the hook. And where's the accountability? Consumers don't just need an assurance that when they offset their emissions, their money is spent on projects that have genuine carbon dioxide emission reduction, they need to understand how it all works.

# trees vs. new technologies

We need more trees to pump oxygen back into the atmosphere, that's clear. Twenty per cent of carbon emissions each year are from deforestation and forest fires, which means that tree planting is an answer, but only part of it. I could always plant a few in my garden to offset my annual trip to India, which pumps out 4.80 tonnes of carbon dioxide, or pay £36 ($71.15) to a company that would do it for me. But which of the two is better for the environment and which would make me feel better? I have the luxury of a garden now but a year ago, I wouldn't have had the option to plant a tree in central London. Some UK companies wouldn't be interested in my garden anyway, protesting that it's the UK government that must present its reduced emission figures to Kyoto, not them. Doing it for them would double-count the figures. Besides, it's not the richer northern hemisphere that needs more trees; it's the poorer, over-polluted, deforested, drought-ridden south. But environmentalists say that large-scale tree planting can damage the environment and livelihoods in the Third World, especially where there is no variety in the species of tree being planted. 'Buying forestry offsets does nothing to lessen society's dependence on fossil fuels, something that is ultimately needed to address climate change,' says Kirsty Clough, of the World Wildlife Fund.

Rather than focus on tree planting alone, many of the carbon offsetting companies do plough our guilt money into funding new technologies. Climate Care, for example, puts some of its money into the Ashden Awards for Sustainable Energy. This means that they are constantly talking to people from all over the world involved with innovative local sustainable-energy schemes.

But with more and more companies coming up with plans to use our cash, the government has been unusually swift to smell a rat. It plans to make the UK the first country with a national standard for testing carbon-offset schemes and warn consumers to be wary of tree-planting offset schemes, suggesting they direct their money instead into 'win-win' projects such as a scheme to generate electricity from pig droppings in Mexico. Justin Francis of responsibletravel.com, which has been offering a carbon-offset scheme with its partner, Climate Care, since early 2001, says,'Choose schemes like funding cleaner wood-burning stoves in India which reduces carbon dioxide emissions, reduces deforestation and causes fewer eye problems.'

The government's standard would be based on the use of certified credits from the established Kyoto market, through sources such as the UN's Clean Development Mechanism. An international framework and a number of institutions back

## travelling responsibly

Responsibletravel.com was the first travel agent to publish a target to reduce total emissions by 60 per cent by 2050. They suggested trying to implement the following when considering your holiday:

- Taking fewer but longer breaks
- Avoiding internal flights in countries where possible
- Booking direct flights (because take-off and landing at stop-over requires a lot of fuel)
- Taking holidays closer to home
- Travelling by train whenever possible

these credits, to ensure that real emission reductions take place, as well as providing a clear audit trail. Some companies in the travel industry, such as First Choice Holidays and lastminute.com, have already undertaken to meet the standard by the end of 2007, when offering the choice to offset to their customers.

'Nearly everything we do in our lives – including breathing – creates carbon dioxide emissions,' says Justin Francis of responsibletravel.com. 'A straw poll we did suggests that people think aviation accounts for around 25 per cent of emissions. But The Stern report says that it accounts for 1.6 per cent of emissions (however as it is more damaging to emit carbon dioxide at altitude this is equivalent to 3.2 per cent of emissions). We all need to do what we can to reduce our total carbon dioxide emissions. By far the biggest source of emissions are our houses (25 per cent) so lagging the loft, using low energy light bulbs, turning down the thermostat one degree, not using the washing machine as much are the biggest things you can do and far more important than stopping flying.'

# slow travel

Flights from Heathrow already pump as much carbon dioxide into the atmosphere as five million cars do every year. Yet the government's aviation expansion plans include building a third runway at Heathrow, which will mean a 70 per cent increase in passengers by 2030 and make the UK's targets on climate change virtually impossible to meet. Looking again at what we have under our noses may well be the answer.

Things have changed since we were kids, and car rides across counties can be an opportunity for some real quality family time, although train travel is always preferable for the environment. *The Rough Guide to Ethical Living* suggests that an average family's annual car use could be offset for as little as £20 ($39.53).

Summers are hotter, the beaches are cleaner and hoteliers seem to actually like children, or at least employ people who do. Cornwall is now a cool surf centre with a Jamie Oliver restaurant and beach bars, and it hosted the Organics Fortnight last year. Wales sells itself on its organic food and stunning coastline, and organic farms across the UK offer Soil Association tours between the tractor rides.

Camping at home doesn't have to be in a conventional tent when there are fully kitted out yurts for hire. You don't have to swim with dolphins; you could try puffins, seals and basking sharks off many of the UK beaches. Even Hoseasons is offering badger watching through night cameras from the comfort of your own holiday cottage. Entrepreneurial ecologists are using their passion for change to invent new types of home- grown holidays in eco-cabins where washable nappies and locally sourced organic food is all provided. Those draughty old mansion houses might inspire you to save energy *and* play like you used to, with pond dipping, free cycling and nature trails all thrown in.

# *spreading the tourism pound*

If you do opt for a package holiday abroad, you'll be less likely to get a grumpy babysitter than an army of board-shorted, nature-loving, water-mad child-carers to look after your baby while you snooze on the beach or learn to sail. Neilson is among some of the more conventional family holiday companies that are using their social responsibility charters to green up what they do best. The idea of creating 'added value' to consumers looking for eco-holidays means that it is in their interest to source local food, rethink their waste policy and focus on more earthy mountain-based activities, spreading the tourism pound among local suppliers such as ski clinics, ice fishing and dog-sledding guides and visits to national wildlife parks. Richard Hammond applauds companies like Neilson and First Choice for these kinds of initiatives, which are getting people out of the hotel lobby shop and encouraging them to spread their money around the local communities.

Most of Neilson's packages are short-haul destinations, although it does now offer ski packages in North America and Canada, but for new parents, they can be the first breather you manage to get since your baby's birth! Holiday companies' baby and kids clubs combined with non-polluting activities like tennis, windsurfing, sailing and skiing, and local food-sourcing policies when you get there can provide a fairly green and a totally relaxing summer or winter holiday.

# *green holiday innovations*

Even if you opt for the high energy pumping, big experiences that lure parents and their kids to far flung outposts, there are still options to slow down once you get there. Instead of flying to Lapland to see Father Christmas, take a train through Sweden from Stockholm (a flight, I know, but hardly a city break) and after flying over the snow on your skidoo, track the local wildlife through ancient forests on snow shoes with a local guide. White pods, a Swiss eco-alternative to chalets, which are heated by a wood-burning stove and insulated with the latest technology, are great fun for kids. They are typical of the innovations inspired by climate change that give holiday makers an opportunity to slow down and to see the world at the pace of a child.

Eco-holidays are not just the wraparound experience that all-inclusive holiday companies have been in the past, where in the pursuit of total relaxation, all the thinking was done for you. It's about waking up to the impact each individual has on the planet. Richard Hammond hosted a webchat about some of the ways we can think green when away from home. One of them stressed the need to remember to take your own water bottle rather than using plastic ones. 'It's bad enough in the UK', Hammond says, 'but many developing countries don't have the resources to deal with the huge increase in the amount of plastic bottles tourism brings in, especially from bottled water.'

Leaving heating and air conditioning off when you leave the hotel room, hanging towels up for use again, and being aware of water shortages are just some of the more obvious ways to holiday responsibly.

# travelling tips

Travelling with a new baby, wherever you go and however you go, means being prepared. You learn from experience, but here are a few tips that might help make your journeys less stressful!

### Hand luggage
Be organized. Make sure that all the right things go in the right bags and that you have what you need with you on a flight. Keeping a baby quiet through a long flight and dealing with his sleep needs when you can't imagine getting through your own is often just too much. When you're breastfeeding, your brain seems to be taking a vacation most of the time anyway. There are countless times when I've forgotten to put the Tushies in the hand luggage and then had a panic attack when I've realized that there is no way that I'm going to find environmentally friendly disposables in the departure lounge!

### Buggies
Buggies, back packs, portable high chairs and child seats can be life-savers when you're travelling; a buggy has storage space, and can hold your extra bags while keeping a sleeping child happy, but there's no way that you can claim that they are green. Unfortunately, they all have to be sprayed with fire retardants that off-gas. A sheepskin stroller liner will keep your child from being in contact with much of the material and it will keep your baby cool in summer and warm in winter.

### Ear pressure

If she wants to travel in her tutu, let her; you'll make more friends with a ballerina in tow than you will with a screaming child! Make sure that you've packed the change of clothes in case she vomits all over her top, and if you're flying, the dummies and comforters you'll need when your baby's ears begin to hurt. If she's got a cold this is particularly important; the pressure will seem unbearable for her – and your fellow passengers. If it looks as if she's getting a cold, try giving her enough garlic and onion to get it out of her system; her screams will be nothing to those on the plane if she flies clogged up with mucus! Swallowing will help to equalize the pressure as well as taking her mind off it. Take sweets for take-off and descent for older kids. It doesn't matter what they do to their teeth for now; sucking stops ears hurting. For younger babies, a bottle or dummy provides perfect sucking material.

### Liquids in the air

These days, air travel can be a nightmare unless you are really organized, thanks to the foiled terrorist plot in London back in August 2006 when the discovery of explosives made from common sport drinks unleashed a whole new level of air travel restrictions. The Transportation Security Administration (TSA) has banned more than 0.8g (3oz) of liquids and gels in hand luggage as well as juices and medicines. Baby formula and breast milk is now allowed in unlimited amounts though, and as long as you are travelling with a baby or toddler, you can take these through the security checkpoints and aboard the plane.

Travelling with your child can be a great opportunity for down time; if you're flying, you may be crossing continents, but while you're strapped in, nobody's going anywhere. Make sure you pack your books – baby books rather than your own is a little more realistic. You won't need toys; a spoon rattling in a plastic cup will provide hours of entertainment!

# safer insect repellents and skin care

When you travel there are the obvious precautions to take such as packing sun lotion and insect repellents. If you can avoid going to countries where vaccinating your baby is necessary, do. His immature immune system will find it hard to cope with such an onslaught. Herbs that an adult might use to stimulate the liver and promote optimum health to avoid vaccinations would not be suitable for a small baby.

# UV protection

If you are heading for somewhere sunny, the best advice for a new baby is to keep him out of strong sunlight between ten in the morning and three in the afternoon, and clothed in breathable fabrics. A hat and sunscreen are essential. With the ozone layer at very risky levels it is especially important in the coming years, and there is increasing evidence linking sunburns at a young age with the risk of developing skin cancer at an older age. Because of the chemical content, many sun blocks are not suitable for babies under six months, and again, herbs offer a gentler option. There are quite a few natural sun lotions formulated for the very sensitive skin of children. Try and find one that has natural UV protection from mineral pigments such as that available from Dr Hauschka, Green People or Lavera. Also make a note that aloe vera, evening primrose or liquorice can calm skin after a hot day out.

Titanium dioxide and zinc oxide are natural ingredients that block out the UVA and UVB rays of the sun but do tend to block the skin's pores. UV suits are readily available in sizes starting from newborn and they do block out the sun's rays and stop sunburn. Sunglasses can also fit the smallest of babies and are especially useful in the snow as they block out harmful ultraviolet rays.

# insect repellent and DEET

As a traveller I never worried too much about the ingredients in my insect repellent; as long as it kept those mosquitoes away, I was happy. But travelling with a baby changes your whole perspective on the subject. Many insect repellents contain

DEET, a very powerful insect repellent that can be dangerous if overused. Most manufacturers recommend that DEET is only sprayed on clothing, never directly on the skin and it should never be used on or nearby children under the age of two.

There are many safe alternatives to DEET-based insect repellents. Essential oil of citronella is a natural alternative and mixed with lavender, chamomile and geranium, can be an effective repellent, but should still be used with caution. Do not let any of the oil come into contact with your child's eyes or mouth. The best way to keep your child bite-free is to use a mosquito net over a travel cot at night and dress him in long sleeves and trousers during the evenings when the mosquitoes are at their worst. If you can, increase his garlic and lemon intake, which will make his skin less attractive to bugs, or your own if you are still breastfeeding.

# guilt-free travel

Travelling is still a wonderful opportunity for the whole family to relax and enjoy each other, whether you're heading off to camp on the coast, cross Europe by train or exotic climes on the other side of the world. Teaching a child to be responsible for his own carbon footprint can be fun; encourage him to eat the local food for example and take him to the markets to see where all the produce comes from. I bet you he'll be able to remember where he first ate moussaka for the rest of his life. A diary packed with souvenirs, foreign words and photos will also remind him of how he spread that tourism pound of yours around the world destinations that rely on it most.

## key principles

You can have great fun planning an eco-holiday or one that allows you to contribute to good carbon offsetting schemes. Choose wisely and when you do travel abroad, think of the impact of your journey on the country you are in and think before you dump any rubbish.

- If you do have to fly, choose an eco-holiday, from tagging turtles off the Great Barrier Reef to community-based tours in Ethiopia

- Encourage the government to invest in renewable energy, cleaner technologies, waste reduction processes and rail transport

- Choose carbon-offsetting schemes like funding cleaner woodburning stoves in India, which reduces deforestation and carbon dioxide emissions

- Look out for the government's quality mark when offsetting; PURE – the Clean Planet Trust, Global Cool, Equiclimate and Carbon Offsets Ltd are among the offsetting providers who already meet the government's standard by offering certified emission reduction credits for their offsetting products

- Book direct flights as take-off and landing for a stop-over requires a lot of fuel and avoid internal flights in countries where you can

- Take holidays closer to home, and travel by train when you can

- Offset the use of the family car. You can do this for as little as £20 ($39.53) per year

- Check to see if your holiday company sources local food, has rethought its waste policy and focuses on spreading the tourism pound among local suppliers

- Don't buy products that are made from endangered plants or wild animals, such as hardwoods, corals, shells, ivory and fur

- Don't throw plastic bottles in bins or drop litter on mountain sides, off chairlifts for example

- Don't disturb wild animals and areas of conservation, like overcrowded dive sites

- Keep your baby out of strong sunlight and clothed in breathable fabrics. A hat and sunscreen are essential, because there is evidence linking sunburns at a young age with the risk of developing skin cancer

# chapter nine

# HOW GREEN IS YOUR CHILDCARE?

# choosing childcare

Choosing the right day nursery or childcare is based on lots of different issues, location, price and space being the most pressing, but what about its philosophy, its recycling policy, its attitude towards food and healthcare? Does it accept a child in washable nappies? How does it deal with disposables? Does it disinfect the place with gender-bending chemicals? If your nursery really is green it could make an enormous difference to your child's mental, social and physical wellbeing.

# what to look for

Nurseries are big business these days commanding fees of up to £250 ($494.20) a week in the bigger cities, so look around to see how well the nursery understands the way small people think. Are there eye-catching displays and plenty of things of interest or beauty on the wall? Children learn just as much through their eyes as they do from their ears, particularly when they are small. A room with plenty of plants, a fish tank or even a goldfish bowl is a nod towards understanding what children love to look at, but look out for nature tables to check if the outside world is being brought inside to inspire them. A budding horse chestnut in a bowl of water is what the more progressive educationalists like Adrienne Campbell, founder of Lewes New School, calls 'meaningful displays', something that a small child can watch and learn from. A pile of plastic toys in the corner will also tell you what you need to know.

## food and waste

Watching children eat is also a great indicator. It's not just that the food and snacks should be home-cooked, locally sourced and organic (one of the 'added values' that no doubt many nurseries will be marketing soon enough) but you should check the way that it is disposed. What happens to all those little glasses of water that are not drunk? Are they emptied down the sink, or are the toddlers encouraged to water the vegetable garden or herb boxes with them? It's the little touches that will tell you more about the school's philosophy than any charter on the wall.

## types of nursery

There are four different types of day nursery that take babies from as young as six weeks to school age:

- Private: independent businesses providing full day care

- Community: fees are generally lower than private nurseries and could use a sliding-scale fee scheme

- Workplace: linked to specific employers who offer places to their staff

- Children's Centres: government subsidized

## outdoor trips

Ask about trips to the local park or other places of interest like city farms and nature reserves. Enquire about sports activities in and out of school. Many nurseries say that they have a health and safety restriction on taking children to the park, but if they have the correct ratio of children to adult, it should be easy enough to organize regular trips out. Children under two should have a 3:1 ratio (although if there are a lot of younger babies in the nursery, it might be necessary to have a ratio of 2:1), two-year-olds, a 4:1 ratio and three- to seven-year-olds, an 8:1 ratio.

## behaviour management policy/procedure

Even if your baby is still small, check out the nursery policy for dealing with bad behaviour; your baby will soak up an aggressive atmosphere like a sponge. By the time a child is three, he will be fighting over that scooter as if his life depended on it, and the way an adult deals with that will have a huge impact on the way he treats conflict in the future. A good nursery with clear boundaries for both staff and children regarding what is expected of them, will not only make your child feel safe but will be a valuable resource for you to draw upon as work your way through parenting's various challenges.

A heavy-handed adult who refuses to listen to both sides of an argument is a child-carer who doesn't think children, however small they are, have a voice. Adrienne Campbell says that 'listening' is what Lewes New School is particularly concerned with, and is at the very heart of the parenting training courses the school runs. 'Even the tiniest children will come up with their own solutions if you give them the opportunity,' she told me. It's also important not to make either one of them wrong or to label them, bad or good.

'The brain can't compute a negative command', says author, osteopath, naturopath and mother of two, Cissi Williams, 'so it is better to say what you want the child to do, rather than what you don't want them to do. Always make sure you tell your child how lovely he is. If he is having a tantrum or behaving in a challenging way, try not to tell him that he is being *naughty* or *stupid*, that he's making you *really angry*. These comments sink into young minds, limiting their beliefs in their unconscious mind. They then start to act on these comments and what you've told them about themselves becomes a self fulfilling prophecy.' However, letting a child know how you are feeling as a result of their behaviour *is* important!

# pastoral care

Tuning into the source of a toddler's anxieties can be a tricky business and can involve some guesswork. 'If your child is not happy, then look at where their needs are not being met,' says Cissi Williams. 'Is she in physical discomfort? Or is she hurting emotionally? Has something upset her? Does she feel as if her place is threatened (such as when a sibling arrives), or that she is not loved equally to her sibling or friend?'

One of the best books to deal with the issue of communication is Adele Faber and Elaine Mazlish's lifesaving book, *How To Talk So Kids Will Listen & Listen So Kids Will Talk*. You don't even have to give in; getting down on your knees as your toddler is screaming blue murder about leaving the playground and saying, 'You don't want to go home yet, and you're sad that we're going, aren't you?' can be just the recognition he needs to give up a tantrum. Similarly with pain, the frustration and fear of the pain not being acknowledged can disappear with a few words. 'Your tummy's sore, isn't it? Ouch, that must really hurt!' will probably do the trick.

But how do you make sure that your childcare professionals are going to use the same language? There are certain short cuts; nurseries following the Steiner and the Montessori principles are based on child-centred philosophies.

# Montessori

Maria Montessori was a paediatrician and pioneered her theories in a children's home in Rome's working-class tenement blocks at the turn of the century. She watched how children acted when left to their own devices. She observed that two-year-olds seemed obsessed by order, always putting chairs under tables and organizing cups and plates at meal times; that kids spontaneously began to write at the age of four and would naturally teach each other in mixed age groups what they had picked up about life. The principles of self-respect, cooperation and understanding seemed to be natural in a child-centred world.

Montessori schools are now found across the UK, Western Europe and America for children from the age of two. 'We encourage children to fasten their own coats and help each other with their shoes,' explains Daisy Cockburn who has been running Brighton's Montessori school for nearly 20 years. 'We encourage them to do things for themselves from the very first day that they're here,' she says. The children spend their days studying the natural world in mixed age groups. The six-year-olds tell the two-year-olds what they know about the ants they are all inspecting and the three-year-olds pitch in with the kind of questions the six-year-olds have forgotten about. What a great way of growing the next generation of environmentalists! A nursery that spends hours of each day teaching your toddler biodiversity of the soil (worms, ants and snails) will do more for the future of the planet than any hot-housing academy for young brains.

Montessori has set the standard in good communication, and you may well find that its 'greeting policy' has been adopted in your favoured nursery, welcoming each child by name as he crosses the threshold, looking him in the eye and shaking his hand. You can tell a good nursery by the way its carers communicate with your child from that very first meeting; it's a sign that respectful communication is at the very core of its philosophy. Ideally, everything else should flow from that first meeting; respect for you as a parent, for other children, colleagues and for their environment is a given.

These Montessori ideals are spreading into the mainstream now and can be applied to use at home too. Montessori consultant, Patricia Winstanley says that although playpens and pushchairs are useful for the parent, if children are left in them for too long, they will be deprived of their need to explore their new skills. 'Pushing them out into the world in front of strangers and traffic is a necessary evil, but it can dull a child's natural sensitivity,' she says. 'Look at how a small child would deal with new information if left to her own devices; notice how long she will sit and gaze at an ant if allowed to do so. Now imagine what happens when she is pushed through a city at top speed. In an ideal world, we would follow the example of the elephant herd which walks at the pace of the baby.'

## the continuum concept

Jean Liedloff's book, *The Continuum Concept: In Search of Happiness Lost*, is one of those must-reads while you're waiting for your life to change forever. It was inspired by Liedloff's observations of a Venezuelan rainforest tribe in which the local children respond naturally to their elders' expectations of them as innately social and cooperative with strong self-preservation instincts. 'Toddlers played together without fighting or arguing, and all the children obeyed their elders instantly and willingly,' writes Liedloff. She was amazed to find that the youngest children of this South American tribe did not cry, cling or appear to be needy in any way. 'The notion of punishing a child had apparently never occurred to these people,' she concluded. 'Nor did their behaviour show anything that could truly be called permissiveness. No child would have dreamed of inconveniencing, interrupting, or being waited on by an adult. And by the age of four, children were contributing more to the work force in their family than they were costing others.'

## Steiner

Steiner schools are based on the philosophy of Rudolph Steiner, who founded his first school in Germany in 1919. There are now nearly 900 Steiner schools around the world and they are influencing mainsteam education.

Children are initially welcomed at the parent and toddler groups where they play, sing and bake bread, while their parents are encouraged to sew, knit and bake as they chat with other parents. Children then move up into the kindergarten when they are three years old.

Nature dictates the rhythm of the school year. Even the smallest children celebrate the cycles of the season with lantern festivals, songs, stories and poems from a rich cultural and spiritual tradition. Each day and each week has its own regular, reassuring rhythm for the children with recurring activities such as ring-time or painting day.

Formal learning is not forced and the natural develoment of the child is protected. A Steiner education is a deep commitment, not just to a different type of education, but to an unusually close relationship with the school. Steiner parents may be seen cleaning, painting and cooking for the school and taking part in a huge amount of fundraising.

Even though Steiner schools offer a broad curriculum, with a great emphasis on creativity, it does have its critics. There are often issues around the lack of early reading and writing, which Steiner schools believe belong to the second seven years of life.

# *attachment parenting*

When the *Continuum Concept* was first published in 1975, it inspired the 'attachment parenting' movement, which suggests that, just like the Venezuelan mothers, we carry our child in a sling until he wants to find his own way. It also suggests that he sleeps in his parents' bed until he wants to leave (often at about two years), and that he is breastfed when wriggling, crying or smacking his lips suggests he's hungry. By positively responding to his cries for attention, the 'attachment parent' is more likely to raise a child whose needs are always met yet who considers himself a worthy member of his social group.

Compare that with the experience of a Western baby's separation from his mother at birth, after medical intervention has brought him screaming into the maternity ward before being bundled into a cot and crying himself to sleep. His natural impulses are then ignored as the clock becomes the new arbiter of his needs, and as he grows, he becomes used to being ignored, being put in a playpen when his mother no longer wants to play with him, and punished if he voices his objection or needs in the only way he can.

Over-protective parents, or carers who project their anxieties on to their children, according to Liedloff, are doing no one in the community a favour. A child who is the centre of attention is bound to have an inflated ego, and can only be disappointed when he finds out that he's been living a fantasy by the time he gets out into the wider world. A child that has been led to believe that he is incapable, innately antisocial and unable to behave without adult input will take on that behaviour. His parents, gods that they are to him, have told him so.

# *responsibility for the planet*

If a child learns to take responsibility for the things around him, doesn't it follow that he will take responsibility for the world that he lives in? Won't life be easier for all of you as you hurtle through his (and relive your) childhood, testing each other's boundaries every second of the way? Doesn't it follow that he will absorb the lessons from a nursery that gets rid of only two bin bags a week after the composting and recycling are done, and grow into a child that automatically wants to do the same at home? Isn't that how we'll get to save the planet?

Remember that waiting lists for nurseries can be long, especially if they are popular. All day nurseries are required by law to be registered and inspected regularly. However, the following are really important points to look out for or to ask when trying to find a green nursery.

• Find out if the nursery uses washable nappies

• Check to see if the nursery has cooking facilities on the premises

• Establish whether the nursery uses organic food and what the nursery policy is on snacks

• Check as to whether the nursery uses green cleaning products

• Find out what their recycling policy is. Do they encourage the toddlers to recycle? Do they recycle unused water after snack time for use in play?

- Has your nursery got a nature table and eye-catching, meaningful displays?

- Ask if the nursery take the children out to the local park or other places of interest

- Does the nursery have wooden or plastic toys?

- How do they greet both of you? A child-carer should greet your child as well as you, even if he is a small baby

- What is the general atmosphere in the nursery? Are the child-carers engaged or bored?

- What is the behaviour management policy? Can you see carers dealing with conflict according to the policy?

# RESOURCES

# baby essentials

## baby basics

- 3 baby sleep gowns
- 6 short-sleeved bodysuits/wrap bodysuits
- 6 long-sleeved bodysuits/wrap bodysuits
- 6 babygros/sleepsuits/playsuits
- 6 bibs
- Cardigan
- 3 hats
- 3 pairs mittens
- 3 pairs booties
- 3 pairs socks
- 4 receiving/swaddling blankets
- 2 double thickness receiving blankets
- 2 baby sleeping bags

## bathtime and nappy changing

- 2–4 hooded towels
- 2 natural sponges (one for face, one for bottom)
- 10 washable wipes/baby washcloths
- Organic cotton wool
- Baby nail scissors
- Talc-free baby powder
- Baby lotion
- Nappy balm
- Petroleum-free jelly
- Baby oil for after bath
- Shampoo/body wash (not for use in first couple of weeks)

## breast- and/or bottle-feeding

- 2–4 nursing bras
- 3–6 sets of washable nursing pads
- 10 muslin squares
- Nipple balm
- Breast pump (manual is greener option)
- Milk storage (bottles or bags)
- Steam sterilizer
- 6 bottles
- Bottle brush
- Nursing pillow (optional but very useful at end of pregnancy to help comfort while sleeping)

## nappies

- A minimum of 16 nappies; we recommend 20–24 so that you can have some in use, some washing and some drying (any less and you end up chasing your tail)
- 4–6 wraps in each size; wraps must fit properly so you need to buy them in newborn, small, medium and large
- Flushable liners, which come in easy tear-off rolls. One pack has 200 liners. If you don't want to use throwaway liners there are washable polyester stay-dry liners available
- A nappy bucket; any bucket with lid can be used
- A pack of two laundry nets; always line the nappy bucket with a laundry net as this saves having to touch the soiled nappies. The net full of nappies can then be lifted straight into the washing machine
- Tea-tree oil. Fill the bucket a third full of water and add a few drops of tea-tree oil. This is a natural antibacterial and kills odours
- Laundry liquid/eco balls

- A biodegradable nappy sanitizer. Every so often put this in the bucket when soaking nappies. This freshens and softens the nappies and gets rid of any stains and can also be used in the washing machine
- Waterproof tote bag: When out and about use this bag to store used nappies until you get home

## *the nursery*

- Moses basket and mattress
- Cot/cotbed and mattress
- Changing table
- Changing mat
- 1–2 mattress pads/protectors
- Mobile
- Musical toy

## *bedding*

- 3–4 fitted sheets
- 2–4 cellular blankets
- Sheepskin

## *travel essentials*

- Baby sling/carriers
- Portable bed
- Buggy or pram
- Sheepskin liner
- Car seat
- Changing bag or portable changing mat

# green directory

## carbon footprint calculator

C Level
Tel: 0870 765 9891
wwwclevel.co.uk/homecalc.html

Erase My Footprint
Paradise Farm
Whitstone
Holsworthy
Devon EX22 6LE
Tel: 01288 341 122
www.erasemyfootprint.com

## carbon offsetting

Carbon Offsets Ltd
13 Market Place
Henley-on-Thames
Oxon RG9 2AA
www.carbon-offsets.com

Carbon Trust
8th Floor
3 Clement's Inn
London WC2A 2AZ
Tel: 0800 085 2005
www.carbontrust.co.uk

Co2Balance Ltd
Bourne House
High Street
Bishops Lydeard
Taunton
Somerset  TA4 3AX
Tel: 0845 094 2620
www.co2balance.com

The CarbonNeutral Company
Bravington House
2 Bravington Walk
Regent Quarter
Kings Cross
London N1 9AF
Tel: 020 7833 6000
www.carbonneutral.com

## clothing

Adili Ltd
Blandford Hill
Milborne St Andrew
Blandford Forum
Dorset DT11 0HZ
Tel: 01258 837 437
www.adili.com

Eddie Bauer
PO Box 7001
Groveport
OH 43125
USA
Tel: 0800 625 7935
www.eddiebauer.com

Edun Apparel Ltd
30–32 Sir John Rogerson's Quay
Dublin 2
Ireland
Tel: 01256 1289
www.edunonline.com

Green Baby
Unit 2Q/R
Leroy House
436 Essex Road
London N1 3QP
Tel: 0870 240 6894
www.greenbaby.co.uk

Howies
Bath House Road
Cardigan
SA43 1JY
Tel: 01239 614 122
www.howies.co.uk

Mountain Equipment Co-op
149 West 4th Avenue
Vancouver
BC V5Y 4A6
Canada
Tel: 001 604 707 3300
www.mec.ca

Patagonia
8550 White Fir Street
PO Box 32050
Reno
NV 89523-2050
USA
Tel: 001 800 638 6464
www.patagonia.com

People Tree Ltd
1st Floor
91–93 Great Eastern Street
London EC2A 3HZ
Tel: 0845 7739 8492; 020 7739 9659
www.ptree.co.uk

Greenfibres
99 High Street
Totnes
Devon
TQ9 5PF
Tel: 01803 868 001
www.greenfibres.com

# complementary health practitioners

Healing People Network
www.healingpeople.com

# eco-products

Buy Organics
54 Broadcroft Avenue
Stanmore
Middx HA7 1PF
Tel: 020 8952 1424
www.buyorganics.co.uk

Earthly Goods
WWF-UK Trading Ltd
PO Box 150
Sandbach
Cheshire CW11 3WB
Tel: 0870 750 7023
www.shop.wwf.org.uk

Eco-Products Inc
3640 Walnut Street
Boulder
CO 80301
USA
Tel: 001 303 449 1876
www.ecoproducts.com

EEMG
c/o Slade and Cooper
6 Mount Street
Manchester M2 5NS
www.ethical-marketing.co.uk

GoGreenLights
10 Strathmore Drive
Charvil
Reading RG10 9QT
Tel: 0800 0 751
www.gogreenlights.co.uk

Green Books Ltd
Foxhole
Dartington
Totnes
Devon TQ9 6EB
Tel: 01803 863 260
www.greenbooks.co.uk

Greenstock
Unit H
Hillcroft Business Park
Whisby Road
Lincoln LN6 3QT
Tel: 0845 2570 444
www.eco-lights.co.uk

The Green Shop/Green Shop Solar
Cheltenham Road
Bisley
Stroud
Glos Gl6 7BX
Tel: 01452 770 629
www.greenshop.co.uk
www.greenshop-solar.co.uk

Natural Collection
Department 7306
Sunderland SR9 9XZ
Tel: 0845 3677 003
Tel: 0191 501 3878
www.naturalcollection.com

Nigel's Eco Store
55 Coleridge Street
Hove BN3 5AB
Tel: 0800 288 8970
www.nigelsecostore.com

## *education*

American Montessori Society
281 Park Avenue South
New York
NY 10010
USA
Tel: 001 212 358 1250
www.amshq.org

Lewes New School
Talbot Terrace
Lewes
East Sussex BN7 2DS
Tel: 01273 477 074
www.lewesnewschool.co.uk

Montessori Centre International
18 Balderton Street
London W1K 6TG
Tel: 020 7493 0165
www.montessori.uk.com

Steiner Waldorf Schools Fellowship
Kidbrooke Park
Forest Row
East Sussex RH18 5JA
Tel: 01342 822 115
www.steinerwaldorf.org.uk

## *environmental issues*

The Clean Planet Trust (PURE)
Hasilwood House
62 Bishopsgate
London EC2N 4AW
Tel: 020 7382 7815
www.puretrust.org.uk

Environment Agency
Rio House
Aztec West
Almondsbury
Bristol BÍ32 4UD
Tel: 08708 506 506
www.environment-agency.gov.uk

Environmental Protection Agency
Ariel Rios Building
1200 Pennsylvania Avenue NW
Washington DC 20460
USA
Tel: 001 202 272 0167
www.epa.gov

Foresight
Bay 327
1 Victoria Street
London SW1H 0ET
Tel: 020 7215 6736
www.foresight.gov.uk

Friends of the Earth
26–28 Underwood Street
London N1 7QJ
Tel: 020 7490 1555
www.foe.co.uk

Greenpeace
Canonbury Villas
London, N1 2PN
Tel: 020 7865 8100
www.greenpeace.org.uk

Housedustmite.org
PO Box 248
East Molesey
Surrey KT8 0YB
Tel: 020 8398 6669
www.housedustmite.org

Pesticide Action Network (PAN)
Development House
56–64 Leonard Street
London EC2A 4JX
Tel: 020 7065 0905
www.pan-uk.org

Rainforest Concern
8 Clanricarde Gardens
London W2 4NA
Tel: 020 7229 2093
www.rainforestconcern.org

REACH (The European Chemicals Bureau)
www.ecb.jrc.it/reach/

Soil Association
South Plaza
Marlborough Street
Bristol
BS1 3NX
Tel: 0117 314 5000
www.soilassociation.org

Stop Climate Chaos
2 Chapel Place
London EC2A 3DQ
Tel: 020 7729 8732
www.stopclimatechaos.org

UNICEF
Africa House
64–78 Kingsway
London WC2B 6NB
Tel: 020 7405 5592
www.unicef.org

Women's Environmental Network (WEN)
PO Box 30626
London E12 1TZ
Tel: 020 7461 9004
www.wen.org.uk

World Health Organisation
Avenue Appia 20
Geneva 27
CH 1211
Switzerland
www.who.int/en

World Wildlife Fund UK
Panda House
Weyside Road
Godalming
Surrey GU7 1XR
Tel: 01483 426 444
www.wwf.org.uk

## food

Country Markets
Dunston House
Dunston Road
Sheepbridge
Chesterfield S41 9QD
Tel: 01246 261 508
www.country-markets.co.uk

Farmersmarket.net
www.farmersmarket.net

Organix Brands Ltd
Knapp Mill
Mill Road
Christchurch
Dorset
BH23 2LU
Tel: 0800 393 511; 01202 479 701
www.organix.com/

Planet Organic
42 Westbourne Grove
London W2 5SH
Tel: 020 7221 7171
www.planetorganic.com

Whole Foods Market
The Barkers Building
63–97 Kensington High Street
London W8 5SE
Tel: 020 7395 7074
www.wholefoodsmarket.com

## *herbalism*

American Herbalists Guild
14 Nob Hill Road
Cheshire
CT 06410
USA
Tel: 001 203 272 6731
www.americanherbalistsguild.com

National Institute of Medical Herbalists
Elm House
54 Mary Arches Street
Exeter EX4 3BA
Tel: 01392 426 022
www.nimh.org.uk

## *homeopathy*

Alliance of Registered Homeopaths
Millbrook
Millbrook Hill
Nutley
East Sussex TN22 3PJ
Tel: 08700 736 339
www.a-r-h.org

Arnica Montana Enterprises Pty Ltd
PO Box 909
Kalamunda
WA 6926
Australia
www.arnica.com.au/index.php

British Homeopathic Association
Hahnemann House
29 Park Street West
Luton
Beds LU21 3BE
Tel: 0870 444 3950
www.trusthomeopathy.org

Helios Homeopathy Ltd
89–97 Camden Road
Tunbridge Wells
Kent TN1 2QR
Tel: 01892 537 254
www.helios.co.uk

Homeopath.co.uk
www.homeopath.co.uk

# nappies

National Association of Nappy Services
www.changeanappy.co.uk

Women's Environmental Network (WEN)
PO Box 30626
London E12 1TZ
Tel: 020 7461 9004
www.wen.org.uk/nappies/index.htm

# natural health

Circaroma
Organic Skin Care Ltd
Unit 6
Aberdeen Business Centre
22 Highbury Grove
London N5 2EA
Tel: 020 7359 1135
www.circaroma.com

Essential Care
26 James Carter Road
Mildenhall
Suffolk IP28 7DE
Tel: 01638 716 593
www.essential-care.co.uk

The Green People Company Limited
Pondtail Farm
Coolham Road
West Grinstead
West Sussex RH13 8LN
Tel: 01403 740 350
www.greenpeople.co.uk

Mooncup Ltd
Dolphin House
40 Arundel Place
Brighton BN2 1GD
Tel: 01273 673 845
www.mooncup.co.uk

Naturally Fabulous
PO Box 348
Keighley
BD20 7WZ
www.naturallyfabulous.co.uk/

Neal's Yard Remedies
Peacemarsh
Gillingham
Dorset SP8 4EU
Tel: 01747 834 600
www.nealsyardremedies.com

The Organic Pharmacy
396 King's Road
London
SW10 0LN
Tel: 020 7351 2232
www.theorganicpharmacy.com

Vital Touch Ltd
Dart Mills
Old Totnes Road
Buckfastleigh
Devon
TQ 11 0NF
Tel: 0845 052 5345
www.vitaltouch.co.uk

## *organic products*

Organic Directory
A Lot of Organics
Unit 55
Milford Road
Reading RG1 8LG
Tel: 0945 094 6498; 0118 950 77 66
www.alotoforganics.co.uk

GoGreen Directory
Cellande House
Gristhorpe Road
Birmingham B29 7SL
Tel: 0121 472 2903
www.gogreen.cellande.co.uk

## *osteopathy*

American Osteopathic Association
142 East Ontario Street
Chicago
IL 60611
USA
Tel: 001 800 621 1773; 001 312 202 8000
www.osteopathic.org

General Osteopathic Council
176 Tower Bridge Road
London SE1 3LU
Tel: 020 7357 6655
www.osteopathy.org.uk

Green Guide Online
Markham Publishing
31 Regal Road
Weasenham Lane Industrial Estate
Wisbech
Cambs PE13 2RQ
Tel: 01945 461 452
www.greenguide.co.uk

The Green Directory Australia
www.thegreendirectory.com.au

## *paints*

Ecos Paints
Unit 34
Heysham Business Park
Middleton Road
Heysham
Lancs LA3 3PP
Tel: 01524 852 371
www.ecospaints.com

## *prenatal care*

Foresight Preconception
178 Hawthorn Road
West Bognor
West Sussex PO21 2UY
Tel: 01243 868 001
www.foresight-preconception.org

## *recycyling*

ActionAid Recycling
14 Kingsland Trading Estate
St Philips Road
Bristol BS2 0JZ
Tel: 0117 304 2390
www.actionaidrecycling.org.uk

Foneback.co.uk
www.foneback.co.uk

Freecycle
www.freecycle.org

Green Metropolis
www.greenmetropolis.com

Office Green Technologies
6 Prospect Way
Hutton
Essex CM13 1XA
Tel: 08700 502 050
www.officegreen.co.uk

Waste and Resources Action Programme (WRAP)
The Old Academy
21 Horse Fair
Banbury
Oxon OX16 0AH
Tel: 0808 100 2040; 01295 819 900
www.wrap.org.uk

# travel

City Car Club
The Busworks
39–41 North Road
London N7 9DP
Tel: 0845 330 1234
www.citycarclub.co.uk

Green Traveller
www.greentraveller.co.uk

Responsible Travel
3rd Floor
Pavilion House
6 Old Steine
Brighton BN1 1EJ
Tel: 01273 600 030
www.responsibletravel.com

Rough Guides UK Ltd
80 The Strand
London WC2R 0RL
Tel: 020 6010 3000
www.roughguides.co.uk

Sailrail
Tel: 0845 755 755
www.sailrail.co.uk

Sustrans
National Cycle Network Centre
2 Cathedral Square

College Green
Bristol BS1 5DD
Tel: 0117 926 8893
www.sustrans.org.uk

Tourism Concern
Stapleton House
277–281 Holloway Road
London N7 8HN
Tel: 020 7133 3330
www.tourismconcern.org.uk

Tribes Travel
Tribes Foundation
12 The Business Centre
Earl Soham
Woodbridge IP13 7SA
Tel: 01728 685 971
www.tribes.co.uk

## *water*

Rainharvesting Systems Ltd
Inchbrook Trading Estate
Bath Road
Woodchester, Stroud
Glos GL5 5EY
Tel: 0845 223 5430
www.rainharvesting.co.uk

Water Green
DroughtBuster UK Ltd
Old School House
Upper Slaughter, Cheltenham
Glos GL54 2JF
Tel: 0870 803 1255
www.droughtbuster.co.uk

# further reading

*Boston Women's Book Collective*, Our Bodies, Our Selves: A New Edition for a New Era, *Touchstone, 2005*

*Duncan Clark*, The Rough Guide to Ethical Living, *Rough Guides, 2005*

*Adele Faber and Elaine Mazlish*, How to Talk So Kids Will Listen & Listen So Kids Will Talk, *Piccadilly Press, 2001*

*Jean Liedloff*, The Continuum Concept: In Search of Happiness Lost, *Addison Wesley, 1986*

*Julian Scott, Ph.D*, Natural Medicine for Children, *Gaia Books, 1990*

*Cissi Williams*, The Well-Being Handbook: An A–Z Guide to Holistic Healing, *Findhorn Press, 2005*

# INDEX

# index

additives, in food 70,
79–80, 97–8
ADHD 70–1
adrenaline 70
Africa 180, 190–1
air-freighted food
87–8
air miles 189, 192
air pollution 69, 74
air travel 200–5, 210–11,
214–15
allergies 48, 63
asthma 68–70
breastfeeding and 49
dust mites 113, 114
food and 76, 77–8
hypoallergenic products
161–2
nickel 93, 178, 197
pollen 147, 150
wheat 51
aluminium 34, 154
amber necklaces 59–60
analgesics 59–60
Anderson, Dr Rosalind C.
142
antibiotics 57, 60
antibodies 55, 62
arrowroot 166

Assisi Sisters of Mary
Immaculate 39–42
asthma 51, 68–70
breastfeeding and
69–70
clothes and 177–8
and disposable nappies
142
food additives and 79
incidence of 48, 63
triggers 69, 103
attachment parenting
227–8

B&Q 107–8
baby: birth trauma 52, 53
digestive system 49–50
essential equipment
232–4
food 75–98
immune system 47–8,
55, 162, 178
learning tastes 89
massage 162–3
nursery 99–126
travelling with 209–11
vaccinations 211
baby wipes 153, 155,
163–5

bacteria 61
bath gels 66, 73
bathrooms see toiletries
baths 44, 119–20, 232
Bechamp, Antoine 61
beds and bedding 37,
   110–17, 126, 234
biodynamic farming 122
birth 53–7
birth trauma 52, 53
bleach 69, 74, 187–8
blinds 119
Blue Skies co-operative,
   Ghana 88
Body Shop 153, 156, 157,
   159
bottle feeding 55, 233
bottles: glass 31, 92–3
   plastic 90, 91, 92, 98,
      208, 216
brain development 79,
   97
breastfeeding 55–7, 233
   and asthma 69–70
   attachment parenting
      227
   benefits of 47, 49, 55, 77
   food and 56
   travel and 209
breathing problems see
   asthma

bubble baths 66, 73, 169,
   172
buggies 209, 224
Bush, George 24, 190
buttons 188

calendula cream 167
Calman, Sir Kenneth 113
Campbell, Adrienne 86,
   218, 220–1
cancer 100, 154, 166, 180,
   212
carbohydrates 97
carbon emissions 27–9,
   87
carbon footprints 38–44,
   101, 105, 200–1
carbon offsetting 189,
   202–6, 214–15
carcinogens 64, 114, 155,
   168
carpets 107, 108, 109
cars 31, 34, 43, 206,
   215
chamomile 159
chemicals 63–5
   and asthma 68
   avoiding 71–2
   build-up in body 77
   in clothes 177
   in cotton 116

in disposable nappies
131, 140–2
food additives 79–80,
97–8
hormone disruptors 77,
79, 91, 92, 140–2, 155,
173
'off-gassing' 68, 118
REACH campaign 105
in toiletries 152–74
see also pesticides
child labour 38, 108, 121,
197
childcare, nurseries
217–30
China 121
cleaning products 69, 74,
101
Climate Care 203, 204
climate change 24–9, 94,
131, 201
clothing: essential items
232
flame retardants 111–12,
176–7
labels 187
manufacture 184–6
organic clothing 31,
38–9, 175–98
retailers 192–6
synthetic materials 177
Clough, Kirsty 203

Cockburn, Daisy 223
coir mattresses 114, 115
colds 51, 210
colic 52, 59, 162
compost 44, 181
computers 100
consumer fear 90
Consumer Products
Safety Commission 104
containers: for food 92–3
recycling 171, 174
Continuum Concept 123,
124, 225, 227
The Cook Report 112–13,
114
Cork, Dr Michael 66
cork flooring 109
Cornwall 206
cot beds 117
cot death 112–13,
115–16, 124
cots 37, 110, 117
mattresses 112–16
cotton 37–42, 83
air miles 189
bedding 126
bleaching 187–8
costs 178–9
Fairtrade 186
mattresses 114–15
organic cotton 31, 38–9,
116, 177–98

pesticides and 180–1,
  182, 187
production in Africa
  190–1
subsidies 190
toys 121, 122
cotton wool 164, 165
coughs 51
councils, and washable
nappies 134–5
Cox, Margaret 67
cradle cap 159–61
cranial osteopathy 52,
  53–4
curtains 119
cutlery, stainless steel 93

dairy products 51
Danish Painters
  Syndrome 103
DEET 212–13
Department for
  Environment, Food and
  Rural Affairs 87, 94
detergents 101, 133
Diamond, Anne 112
diet see food
digestive system 49–50
dioxin 141, 148
diseases 61
dishwashers 43
disinfectants 69, 74

drink containers 92–3
drugs, antibiotics 57, 60
dust mites 113, 114
dyes 187–8

'E' numbers 79, 82
ear pressure, in aircraft
  210
earache 54
eco balls 30–1, 43
eczema 51, 65–7
  chemicals and 154
  clothes and 177–8
  incidence of 48, 63
  and washable nappies
    140
Edible School Yard
  project, San Francisco
  84
Egypt 122, 186, 189
electro-magnetic
  frequencies (EMFs) 100
Employment Generation
  and Marketing Mission
  (EGMM) 184–5
energy: reducing use of
  28–9, 100
  underfloor heating 107
  washing nappies 136,
    149
Environment Agency 129,
  136

Essential Care 156–7
essential oils 160–1, 162
European Union 135, 155, 168, 174

Faber, Adele 222
faddy eating 89
faeces: changing nappies 145
  in landfill sites 128–9
Fairtrade 37–8, 39, 41, 76, 95, 122, 185–7, 191, 192–6, 198
farmers' markets 95
farming 83, 122, 180–3
fear, consumer 90
fevers 74
fish oil 79
flame retardants 103, 109, 111–12, 114, 115, 176–7
flannelette nappies 147, 149
flavour enhancers 80
flaxseed oil 79, 82
flooring 29, 106–9, 125
fluoride toothpaste 170
food 75–98
  additives 70, 79–80, 97–8
  air-freight 87–8
  and allergies 76, 77–8
  and breastfeeding 56, 57
  changing diet 81–2
  consumer fear 90
  containers 92–3
  digestive system 49–50
  eating as a family 88–9
  hormone disruptors in 91
  local food 87–8, 95–6
  in nurseries 219
  organic food 81, 82–6
  retailing 36
Food Commission 80
food miles 87, 189, 192
Foresight 80
Forest Stewardship Council (FSC) 108
formaldehyde 107, 110, 118, 177
Francis, Justin 201, 203–4, 205
Fraser, Romy 159
Friends of the Earth (FOE) 77, 82, 103, 108
fruit 49–50, 73, 77, 82, 87–8, 97
furniture 110–11
futons 114

germs 61
Ghana 88

glass: bottles 31, 92–3
  eco-homes 109
global warming 24–9, 94,
  131, 201
glues 107, 110, 118
gluten 76
GM cotton 191
Gore, Al 9, 24
grains 97
Green Baby 18–20
Greenpeace 27–8, 64, 92,
  103, 105–9, 141, 153

H&M 41, 194
Hammond, Richard
  200–1, 207, 208
Harris, Dr Gill 89
hay fever 48, 63
Heathrow Airport 205
heating 28–9, 107
Hellberg, Helge 86
hemp oil 106
herbs 57–9, 158–61
holidays 200–1, 204–15
homeopathy 53, 54, 57–9
hormone disruptors 77,
  79, 91, 92, 140–2, 155,
  173
hyperactivity 70–1, 79
hypersensitivity 70–1
hypoallergenic products
  161–2

Ikea 108
illness 50–2, 61, 64–5
immune system 47–8, 50,
  178
  baby massage and 162
  breastfeeding and 55
  eczema 67
  vaccinations 60–2, 211
India 39, 88, 180–2,
  184–5, 186, 189, 202,
  204
infertility 140
insect repellents 211,
  212–13
insulation 28, 44
International Institute of
  Environment and
  Development (IIED) 190

Kenya 87–8
Kyoto University 154

labels: on clothes 187
  on toiletries 171, 172–3
landfill sites 128, 132, 135,
  144, 148
latex mattresses 114, 115
laundry services 132–4,
  145
lead poisoning 102,
  104
Leahy, Sir Terry 84

Lewes New School 218, 220–1
Liedloff, Jean 123, 225, 227–8
Limerick, Countess of 113
liners, nappy 145, 233
Link, Ann 136
local food 87–8, 95–6
Lund University 155
Lush 155–6
lymphatic system 163

Maack, Thilo 141
magnesium 79, 97
male infertility 140
manufacturing industry 34–5
Marin County, California 84–6
Marks & Spencer 36, 41, 182, 187
massage, baby 162–3
mattresses 37, 112–16
Mazlish, Elaine 222
mealtimes 88–9
medicine 50–1, 57–9
menstruation, Mooncup 31
methane 128–9
milk baths 159
mites, dust 113, 114

Monbiot, George 201
Monsanto 191
Montessori schools 121, 222, 223–4
Mooncup 31
Moses baskets 117
mosquitoes 212–13
myelin 162

nappies, disposable 128–39
  changing 232
  chemicals in 140–2
  costs 130, 137, 138
  and eczema 140
  gel filling 12–14
  green versions 143–4
  in landfill sites 128–9, 132, 135, 144, 148
nappies, washable 14–17, 31, 129–39
  changing 144–6, 232
  costs 130, 137, 138
  energy use 149
  essentials 233–4
  fabrics 147
  laundry services 132–4, 145
  nappy systems 146–7
  types of 145
nappy rash 12–14, 140, 159, 167

National Consumer
  Council 36
naturopathy 50–1, 54
Neal's Yard 158, 159
necklaces, amber 59–60
Neilson 207
nervous system 162
New Zealand 84, 124
Next 194
nickel allergy 93, 178, 197
Nike 41
nurseries 218–30
  behaviour management
    220–1
  food in 219
  Montessori schools 222,
    223–4
  outdoor trips 220
  pastoral care 222
  Steiner schools 222,
    226–7
  types of 219
nursery, baby's 99–126
  baby baths 119–20
  beds 110–17
  curtains and blinds 119
  essentials 234
  flooring 106–9, 125
  furniture 110–11
  Moses baskets 117
  paints 103–6, 125
  toys 120–2

  wallpapers 118
nut allergy 78

Oakland, California 86
oestrogen mimics 155
'off-gassing', chemicals
  68, 118
oil 26–7, 34, 38, 82, 94
oils, essential 160–1, 162
omega 3 fatty acids 79,
  82, 97
organochlorides 191
osteopathy, cranial 52,
  53–4
ozone 101, 212

packaging 91, 93, 189
painkillers 59–60
paints 101, 103–6, 125
pants, nappy 146
parabens 154, 155–6, 172
Pasteur, Louis 61
peanut allergy 78
Pesticide Action Network
  (PAN) 190, 191, 193, 194
pesticides 38, 42
  in baby food 49–50
  in cotton 37, 116, 180–1,
    182, 187
  in fruit and vegetables
    48, 77, 82
  organochlorides 191

in water 83

petroleum jelly 168–9, 174

phosphates 70, 133

phthalates 91, 92, 98, 118, 154–5, 173

plasticizers 107

plastics: and asthma 142

bottles 90, 91, 92, 98, 208, 216

buttons 188

packaging 91, 93, 189

recycling 34, 189

playpens 224, 228

polar bears 131

pollen allergy 147, 150

pollution 47–8, 69, 74

Porritt, Jonathan 26, 81

potty training 139, 167

poverty, in developing countries 191

powder, talcum 166, 173

preservatives: in food 79–80, 97–8

in toiletries 154, 155–8

Procter & Gamble 137, 141

propylene glycol stearate 154

protein, in breast milk 55

Purmann, Gina 132

pushchairs 209, 224

PVC 98, 107, 125

REACH report 64, 105, 153

Real Nappy Association (RNA) 15–16, 130, 138–9

recycling 33–4

beds 116

containers 171, 174

plastics 34, 189

reduce 33

reflexology 163

respiratory problems 51, 103, 106–7

responsibletravel.com 201, 202–3

retailers 34–6, 192–6

reuse 32–3

Roddick, Anita 153, 159

Rolf, Gina 155–6

rubber 110–11

rugs 108

scalp, cradle cap 159–61

Schwarzenegger, Arnold 153

Scott, Julian 57

seasonal affective disorder (SAD) 29

Sekem 122

shampoos 169, 172

sheepskins 123–4, 209

Shenoy, Meera 184–5
Shiva, Vandana 87–8
shopping 34–6, 82, 95
showers 44
Sick Building Syndrome 103
SIDS (Sudden Infant Death Syndrome) 112–13, 115–16
Simmons, Shelley 156
skin: nappy rash 12–14, 140, 159, 167
   pesticides and 48
   sun protection 212, 216
   toiletries 152
   see also eczema
slings 124, 227
smell, sense of 89
soaps 169
sodium lauryl sulphate (SLS) 154, 155, 169, 172
soil, organic farming 83, 85, 181
Soil Association (SA) 82, 87–8, 154, 158, 171, 188, 206
solar power 29
solid foods 89
soya products 87
spider plants 110
Spoor, Gijs 180–1, 182
stainless steel cutlery 93

stains, on washable nappies 145, 149
Steiner schools 222, 226–7
Stern Report 205
subsidies, cotton production 190
sun protection 212, 216
sunglasses 212
super-absorbent polymers (SAPs) 141
supermarkets 36, 82, 85, 86, 95
supply chains 102, 166, 190
surfactants 66, 73
Sweden 208

talcum powder 166, 173
tantrums 221, 222
tastes, learning 89
TBT (tributylin) 141–2
teething 59
temperatures 74
terry nappies 146, 147
Tesco 36, 41, 194
testicles 140
Thomas, Joan 169
tiles, floor 109
toiletries 152–74
   baby powder 166, 173
   baby wipes 163–5

herbs 158–61
hypoallergenic products 161–2
labels 171, 172–3
petroleum-based products 168–9
preservatives 154, 155–8
soaps and shampoos 169, 172
toothpaste 170, 172
toilets 44
toothbrushes 170
toothpaste 170, 172
Top Shop 194
Toulmin, Camilla 190
tourism 200–1, 204–15
toys 120–2
trains 200, 201, 208
Transition Towns 86
travel 199–215
  air travel 200–5, 210–11, 214–15
  carbon offsetting 202–5
  essentials 234
  food miles 87, 189, 192
  green holidays 208
  insect repellents 211, 212–13
  rail travel 200, 201, 208
  tips 209–11
  tourism 200–1, 204–15
  UV protection 212

trees, carbon offsetting 202–3
Tropical Forest Trust 108
tumble dryers 43, 147
Tushies 143, 144, 165

Under the Nile 122, 186
underfloor heating 107
UNICEF 108
United Nations 204
UV protection 212, 216

vaccinations 60–2, 71–2, 211
Vann, Lizzie 76
vegetables 73, 97
  air-freighted food 87–8
  pesticide residues 49–50, 77, 82
viruses 61, 128, 148
Vogel, Alfred 159
volatile organic compounds (VOCs) 68, 101, 103, 105, 109, 118, 125

Waitrose 85, 95
Wales 206
wallpapers 118
washing: bedding 126
  eco balls 30–1, 43
  nappies 133, 136, 145

washing machines 43–4
waste 32, 36–7, 127–50
water: drinking 44
  pesticides in 83
Waters, Alice 84
Weeds, Abi 156–7
wheat allergy 51
*Which?* magazine 83
Whole Foods 36
Williams, Cissi 52, 221, 222
Wilson, Dr Richard 115–16
windows, size of 29
Winstanley, Patricia 224
wipes 153, 155, 163–5
Women's Environmental Network (WEN) 15–16, 130–4, 136–9, 141–2, 153, 154, 155
wood: floors 107–8
  furniture 110–11
  toys 122
wool, mattresses 115
World Bank 184
World Health Organization (WHO) 27–8, 128, 142
World Wildlife Fund (WWF) 64, 91, 103, 108, 203
worms 44, 181

wraps, nappy 146, 233

yogurt 60

Zameen Organics 88, 180–1, 182
zinc 79, 97
zirconium 154

# acknowledgements

To the many people who took a risk and set up their businesses because they believed in the bigger picture. In India, Kirsten Weihe Keidel of Sense Organics, Satish Chukkapilli of Textilestation, Gijs Spoor of Zameen Organics and Sister Michael and all the Sisters of Assisi at Assisi Garments.

Thanks to Katie Whitehouse at Vital Touch, Nick Campeau at Neal's Yard Remedies in Brighton, and Abi Woods at Essential Care for their advice and insights.

Thanks to Craig Sams, Jemima Roberts and Clio Turton of the Soil Association, Adrienne Campbell of The Lewes New School and Transition Town Lewes, Justin Francis of Responsible Travel and Richard Hammond of www.greentraveller.com.

Thanks to all the employees of Green Baby, past and present without whom I couldn't have done this. Also my gratitude to all the suppliers and companies that I have worked with over the years that managed to teach me so much along the way.